STAAR Grade 3

Summer Math Workbook

Essential Summer Learning Math Skills plus Two Complete STAAR Math Practice Tests

By

Michael Smith & Reza Nazari

STAAR Grade 3 Summer Math Workbook

Published in the United State of America By

The Math Notion

Web: WWW.MathNotion.Com

Email: info@Mathnotion.com

About the Author

Michael Smith has been a math instructor for over a decade now. He holds a master's degree in Management. Since 2006, Michael has devoted his time to both teaching and developing exceptional math learning materials. As a Math instructor and test prep expert, Michael has worked with thousands of students. He has used the feedback of his students to develop a unique study program that can be used by students to drastically improve their math score fast and effectively.

– **ACT Math Practice Book**

– **SAT Math Practice Book**

– **PSAT Math Practice Book**

– **ISEE Math Practice Books**

– **Common Core Math Practice Books**

– **many Math Education Workbooks, Exercise Books and Study Guides**

As an experienced Math teacher, Mr. Smith employs a variety of formats to help students achieve their goals: He tutors online and in person, he teaches students in large groups, and he provides training materials and textbooks through his website and through Amazon.

You can contact Michael via email at:

info@Mathnotion.com

Prepare for the STAAR Math test with a perfect workbook!

STAAR Summer Math Workbook is a learning math workbook to prevent Summer learning loss. It helps students retain and strengthen their Math skills and provides a strong foundation for success. This workbook provides students with solid foundation to get a head starts on their upcoming school year.

STAAR Summer Math Workbook is designed by top test prep experts to help students prepare for the STAAR Math test. It provides test-takers with an in-depth focus on the math section of the test, helping them master the essential math skills that test-takers find the most troublesome. This is a prestigious resource for those who need an extra practice to succeed on the STAAR Math test in the summer.

STAAR Summer Math Workbook contains many exciting and unique features to help your student scores higher on the STAAR Math test, including:

- Over 2,500 of standards-aligned math practice questions with answers
- Complete coverage of all Math concepts which students will need to ace the STAAR test
- Content 100% aligned with the latest STAAR test
- Written by STAAR Math experts
- 2 full-length STAAR Math practice tests (featuring new question types) with detailed answers

This Comprehensive Summer Workbook for the STAAR Math is a perfect resource for those STAAR Math test takers who want to review core content areas, brush-up in math, discover their strengths and weaknesses, and achieve their best scores on the STAAR test.

WWW.MathNotion.COM

… So Much More Online!

✓ FREE Math Lessons

✓ More Math Learning Books!

✓ Mathematics Worksheets

✓ Online Math Tutors

For a PDF Version of This Book

Please Visit WWW.MathNotion.com

Contents

Chapter 1: Place Values and Number Sense

Topics that you'll learn in this chapter:

- ✓ Place Values

- ✓ Compare Numbers

- ✓ Numbers in Word

- ✓ Roman Numerals

- ✓ Rounding

- ✓ Odd or Even

- ✓ Rounding and Estimating

- ✓ Estimate Sums

- ✓ Estimate Differences

- ✓ Estimate Products

- ✓ Missing Numbers

Place Values

✎ Write numbers in expanded form.

1) Sixty–two   ___ + ___

2) fifty–six   ___ + ___

3) thirty–one   ___ + ___

4) forty–five   ___ + ___

5) twenty–eight   ___ + ___

✎ Circle the correct choice.

6) The 6 in 56 is in the

         Ones place   tens place   hundreds place

7) The 2 in 25 is in the

         Ones place   tens place   hundreds place

8) The 9 in 918 is in the

         Ones place   tens place   hundreds place

9) The 3 in 537 is in the

         Ones place   tens place   hundreds place

10) The 9 in 289 is in the

         Ones place   tens place   hundreds place

Comparing and Ordering Numbers

✍ Use less than, equal to or greater than.

1) 31 _____ 33

2) 57 _____ 49

3) 92 _____ 88

4) 76 _____ 67

5) 43 _____ 43

6) 54 _____ 46

7) 97 _____ 88

8) 42 _____ 36

9) 55 _____ 55

10) 57 _____ 75

11) 28 _____ 38

12) 19 _____ 15

13) 82 _____ 90

14) 78 _____ 84

✍ Order each set numbers from least to greatest.

15) – 18, – 22, 28, – 17, 4   ___, ___, ___, ___, ___, ___

16) 19, –36, 11, – 12, 5   ___, ___, ___, ___, ___, ___

17) 27, – 56, 20, 1, – 27   ___, ___, ___, ___, ___, ___

18) 26, – 96, 2, – 26, 87, –75   ___, ___, ___, ___, ___, ___

19) –10, –71, 70, –26, –59, –39   ___, ___, ___, ___, ___, ___

20) 88, 4, 38, 7, 78, 9   ___, ___, ___, ___, ___, ___

21) 84, 14, 24, 0, 35, 22   ___, ___, ___, ___, ___, ___

Numbers in Word Form

✏️ Write each number in words.

1) 372 _____

2) 605 _____

3) 550 _____

4) 351 _____

5) 793 _____

6) 647 _____

7) 3,219 _____

8) 5,326 _____

9) 2,842 _____

10) 4,691 _____

11) 5,531 _____

12) 7,360 _____

13) 2,532 _____

14) 8,014 _____

15) 11,242 _____

Roman Numerals

✍ Write in Romans numerals.

1	I	11	XI	21	XXI
2	II	12	XII	22	XXII
3	III	13	XIII	23	XXIII
4	IV	14	XIV	24	XXIV
5	V	15	XV	25	XXV
6	VI	16	XVI	26	XXVI
7	VII	17	XVII	27	XXVII
8	VIII	18	XVIII	28	XXVIII
9	IX	19	XIX	29	XXIX
10	X	20	XX	30	XXX

1) 11 _____

2) 21 _____

3) 24 _____

4) 16 _____

5) 27 _____

6) 29 _____

7) 12 _____

8) 28 _____

9) 15 _____

10) 20 _____

11) Add 16 + 14 and write in Roman numerals. _____

12) Subtract 34 − 5 and write in Roman numerals. _____

Rounding Numbers

📌 Round each number to the underlined place value.

1) 3,<u>7</u>93

2) 3,<u>8</u>76

3) 34<u>5</u>2

4) 7,1<u>9</u>3

5) 5,2<u>7</u>8

6) 1,4<u>7</u>7

7) 8,<u>3</u>13

8) 24.<u>6</u>8

9) 8<u>4</u>.92

10) 71.<u>3</u>4

11) 664.7

12) <u>9</u>,135

13) 15.3<u>8</u>1

14) 4,<u>5</u>21

15) 3<u>6</u>.50

16) 4,<u>8</u>19

17) 6,6<u>8</u>5

18) 2,5<u>3</u>8

19) 73.<u>6</u>2

20) 16,<u>5</u>27

21) 2<u>9</u>.720

22) 12,3<u>6</u>6

23) 31,<u>7</u>29

24) 7,8<u>3</u>8

Odd or Even

📝 Identify whether each number is even or odd.

1) 18 _____   7) 80 _____

2) 27 _____   8) 53 _____

3) 21 _____   9) 58 _____

4) 17 _____   10) 98 _____

5) 67 _____   11) 49 _____

6) 76 _____   12) 113 _____

📝 Circle the even number in each group.

13) 52, 11, 35, 73, 5, 29   15) 33, 45, 86, 59, 63, 87

14) 13, 15, 113, 87, 71, 18   16) 55, 32, 79, 51, 21, 83

📝 Circle the odd number in each group.

17) 54, 36, 48, 76, 71, 100   19) 58, 92, 25, 78, 76, 50

18) 32, 56, 40, 74, 98, 67   20) 89, 12, 88, 42, 48, 120

Rounding and Estimating

✎ Round each number to the underlined place value.

1) <u>9</u>19

2) 3,<u>9</u>23

3) 8<u>5</u>6

4) <u>7</u>8

5) <u>7</u>2

6) 5<u>6</u>3

7) 4,<u>8</u>45

8) 7.<u>4</u>7

9) 6.<u>8</u>76

10) 2<u>4</u>.421

✎ Estimate the sum by rounding each added to the nearest ten.

11) 58 + 7

12) 16 + 63

13) 73 + 6

14) 46 + 19

15) 12 + 86

16) 28 + 13

17) 37 + 93

18) 47 + 9

19) 36 + 83

20) 23 + 69

21) 11 + 73

22) 63 + 41

23) 52 + 76

24) 35 + 85

25) 752 + 131

26) 526 + 144

Estimate Sums

⬛Estimate the sum by rounding each added to the nearest ten.

1) $56 + 8$

2) $19 + 63$

3) $73 + 6$

4) $16 + 47$

5) $13 + 53$

6) $37 + 16$

7) $29 + 87$

8) $56 + 6$

9) $43 + 59$

10) $54 + 55$

11) $26 + 43$

12) $22 + 81$

13) $34 + 65$

14) $71 + 15$

15) $526 + 356$

16) $64 + 61$

17) $92 + 74$

18) $19 + 99$

19) $48 + 95$

20) $43 + 25$

21) $71 + 58$

22) $26 + 91$

23) $32 + 76$

24) $52 + 29$

Estimate Differences

✎ Estimate the difference by rounding each number to the nearest ten.

1) 55 – 11

2) 33 – 22

3) 55 – 26

4) 43 – 23

5) 78 – 46

6) 52 – 21

7) 87 – 57

8) 47 – 29

9) 93 – 49

10) 56 – 47

11) 77 – 21

12) 65 – 17

13) 49 – 22

14) 69 – 27

15) 72 – 48

16) 66 – 41

17) 91– 49

18) 28 – 12

19) 54 – 43

20) 87 – 35

21) 86 – 58

22) 69 – 41

23) 89– 12

24) 96 – 27

Estimate Products

✏️ Estimate the products.

1) 16 × 17

2) 25 × 22

3) 24 × 18

4) 42 × 19

5) 57 × 32

6) 35 × 67

7) 43 × 76

8) 27 × 33

9) 29 × 46

10) 75 × 24

11) 62 × 53

12) 71 × 42

13) 28 × 31

14) 69 × 48

15) 45 × 77

16) 53 × 63

17) 24 × 85

18) 37 × 29

19) 24 × 48

20) 62 × 85

21) 89 × 52

22) 75 × 18

23) 52 × 15

24) 89 × 67

Missing Numbers

🖎 Find the missing numbers.

1) $30 \times \underline{} = 120$

2) $26 \times \underline{} = 78$

3) $\underline{} \times 15 = 75$

4) $18 \times \underline{} = 108$

5) $\underline{} \times 14 = 98$

6) $19 \times \underline{} = 114$

7) $\underline{} \times 3 = 45$

8) $33 \times \underline{} = 99$

9) $35 \times \underline{} = 140$

10) $14 \times 6 = \underline{}$

11) $17 \times 8 = \underline{}$

12) $25 \times 2 = \underline{}$

13) $28 \times 5 = \underline{}$

14) $\underline{} \times 32 = 160$

15) $25 \times \underline{} = 150$

16) $28 \times 7 = \underline{}$

17) $30 \times \underline{} = 240$

18) $12 \times \underline{} = 108$

19) $\underline{} \times 13 = 78$

20) $22 \times 7 = \underline{}$

21) $\underline{} \times 32 = 256$

22) $16 \times \underline{} = 80$

23) $31 \times 6 = \underline{}$

24) $27 \times 11 = \underline{}$

25) $\underline{} \times 19 = 133$

26) $52 \times \underline{} = 104$

Answers of Worksheets – Chapter 1

Place Values

1) 60 + 2
2) 50 + 6
3) 30 + 1
4) 40 + 5
5) 20 + 8
6) ones place
7) tens place
8) hundreds place
9) tens place
10) one place

Comparing and Ordering Numbers

1) 31 less than 33
2) 57 greater than 49
3) 92 greater than 88
4) 76 greater than 67
5) 43 equals to 43
6) 54 greater than 46
7) 97 greater than 88
8) 42 greater than 36
9) 55 equals to 55
10) 57 less than 75
11) 28 less than 38
12) 19 greater than 15
13) 82 less than 90
14) 78 less than 84
15) –22, –18, –17, 4, 28
16) –36, –12, 5, 11, 19
17) –56, –27, 1, 20, 27
18) –96, –75, –26, 2, 26, 87
19) –71, –59, –39, –26, –10, 70
20) 4, 7, 9, 38, 78, 88
21) 0, 14, 22, 24, 35, 84

Numbers in Word Form

1) three hundred seventy-two
2) six hundred five
3) five hundred fifty
4) three hundred fifty-one
5) seven hundred ninety -three
6) six hundred forty- seven
7) three thousand, two hundred nineteen
8) five thousand, three hundred twenty-six
9) two thousand, eight hundred forty-two
10) four thousand, six hundred ninety-one
11) five thousand, five hundred thirty-one
12) seven thousand, three hundred sixty
13) two thousand, five hundred thirty-two
14) eight thousand, fourteen
15) eleven thousand, two hundred forty-two

Roman Numerals

1) XI
2) XXI
3) XXIV
4) XVI
5) XXVII
6) XXIX
7) XII
8) XXVIII
9) XV
10) XX
11) XXX
12) XXIX

Rounding Numbers

1) 3,800
2) 4,000
3) 3,450
4) 7,190
5) 5,280
6) 1,480
7) 8,300
8) 24.70
9) 85.00
10) 71.30
11) 665.00
12) 9,000

13) 15.380	16) 4,800	19) 73.60	22) 12,370
14) 4,500	17) 6,700	20) 16,500	23) 31,700
15) 37.00	18) 2,540	21) 30.00	24) 7,840

Odd or Even

1) even	6) even	11) odd	16) 32
2) odd	7) even	12) odd	17) 71
3) odd	8) odd	13) 52	18) 67
4) odd	9) even	14) 18	19) 25
5) odd	10) even	15) 86	20) 89

Rounding and Estimating

1) 900	10) 24	19) 120
2) 3,900	11) 70	20) 90
3) 860	12) 80	21) 80
4) 80	13) 80	22) 100
5) 70	14) 70	23) 130
6) 560	15) 100	24) 130
7) 4,800	16) 40	25) 880
8) 7.5	17) 130	26) 670
9) 6.9	18) 60	

Estimate sums

1) 70	9) 100	17) 160
2) 80	10) 110	18) 120
3) 80	11) 70	19) 150
4) 70	12) 100	20) 70
5) 60	13) 100	21) 130
6) 60	14) 90	22) 120
7) 120	15) 890	23) 120
8) 70	16) 120	24) 80

Estimate differences

1) 50	3) 30	5) 30
2) 10	4) 20	6) 30

7) 30

8) 20

9) 40

10) 10

11) 60

12) 50

13) 30

14) 40

15) 20

16) 30

17) 40

18) 20

19) 10

20) 50

21) 30

22) 30

23) 80

24) 70

Estimate products

1) 400

2) 600

3) 400

4) 800

5) 1,800

6) 2,800

7) 3,200

8) 900

9) 1,500

10) 1,600

11) 3,000

12) 2,800

13) 900

14) 3,500

15) 4,000

16) 3,000

17) 1,800

18) 1,200

19) 1,000

20) 5,400

21) 4,500

22) 1,600

23) 1,000

24) 6,300

Missing Numbers

1) 4

2) 3

3) 5

4) 6

5) 7

6) 6

7) 15

8) 3

9) 4

10) 84

11) 136

12) 50

13) 140

14) 5

15) 6

16) 196

17) 8

18) 9

19) 6

20) 154

21) 8

22) 5

23) 186

24) 297

25) 7

26) 2

Chapter 2:

Adding and Subtracting

Topics that you'll learn in this chapter:

- ✓ Adding Two–Digit Numbers

- ✓ Subtracting Two–Digit Numbers

- ✓ Adding Three–Digit Numbers

- ✓ Adding Hundreds

- ✓ Adding 4–Digit Numbers

- ✓ Subtracting 4–Digit Numbers

Adding Two–Digit Numbers

✎ Find each sum.

1)
$$\begin{array}{r} 84 \\ +\ 12 \\ \hline \end{array}$$

2)
$$\begin{array}{r} 23 \\ +\ 18 \\ \hline \end{array}$$

3)
$$\begin{array}{r} 64 \\ +\ 24 \\ \hline \end{array}$$

4)
$$\begin{array}{r} 19 \\ +\ 19 \\ \hline \end{array}$$

5)
$$\begin{array}{r} 66 \\ +\ 34 \\ \hline \end{array}$$

6)
$$\begin{array}{r} 41 \\ +\ 26 \\ \hline \end{array}$$

7)
$$\begin{array}{r} 74 \\ +\ 8 \\ \hline \end{array}$$

8)
$$\begin{array}{r} 49 \\ +\ 37 \\ \hline \end{array}$$

9)
$$\begin{array}{r} 70 \\ +\ 20 \\ \hline \end{array}$$

10)
$$\begin{array}{r} 81 \\ +\ 12 \\ \hline \end{array}$$

11)
$$\begin{array}{r} 69 \\ +\ 11 \\ \hline \end{array}$$

12)
$$\begin{array}{r} 89 \\ +\ 35 \\ \hline \end{array}$$

13)
$$\begin{array}{r} 91 \\ +\ 13 \\ \hline \end{array}$$

14)
$$\begin{array}{r} 77 \\ +\ 33 \\ \hline \end{array}$$

Subtracting Two–Digit Numbers

✎ Find each difference.

1) 19
   −8
   ───

2) 25
   − 16
   ───

3) 32
   − 19
   ───

4) 25
   − 25
   ───

5) 58
   − 23
   ───

6) 60
   − 10
   ───

7) 71
   − 48
   ───

8) 65
   − 31
   ───

9) 72
   − 41
   ───

10) 96
    − 66
    ───

11) 99
    − 84
    ───

12) 73
    − 43
    ───

13) 51
    − 27
    ───

14) 82
    − 12
    ───

Adding Three–Digit Numbers

✎ Find each sum.

1)
$$411 \atop + \ 26$$
———

2)
$$653 \atop + 241$$
———

3)
$$741 \atop + 357$$
———

4)
$$678 \atop + 222$$
———

5)
$$129 \atop + 111$$
———

6)
$$498 \atop + 220$$
———

7)
$$637 \atop + 120$$
———

8)
$$593 \atop + 648$$
———

9)
$$895 \atop + 134$$
———

10)
$$479 \atop + 139$$
———

11)
$$795 \atop + 343$$
———

12)
$$918 \atop + 527$$
———

13)
$$897 \atop + 365$$
———

14)
$$911 \atop + 199$$
———

Adding Hundreds

Add.

1) $200 + 300 =$ ——

2) $200 + 500 =$ ——

3) $700 + 700 =$ ——

4) $600 + 400 =$ ——

5) $300 + 800 =$ ——

6) $600 + 600 =$ ——

7) $800 + 900 =$ ——

8) $900 + 700 =$ —

9) $500 + 800 =$ —

10) $200 + 700 =$ ——

11) $900 + 900 =$ ——

12) $600 + 900 =$ ——

13) $100 + 500 =$ ——

14) $200 + 800 =$ ——

15) If there are 900 balls in a box and Jackson puts 700 more balls inside, how many balls are in the box?

_____ balls

Adding 4–Digit Numbers

✎ Add.

1) $\begin{array}{r} 2,426 \\ +\,5,394 \\ \hline \end{array}$

3) $\begin{array}{r} 2,530 \\ +\,1,363 \\ \hline \end{array}$

5) $\begin{array}{r} 8,864 \\ +1,256 \\ \hline \end{array}$

2) $\begin{array}{r} 6,256 \\ +\,2,893 \\ \hline \end{array}$

4) $\begin{array}{r} 7,150 \\ +2,673 \\ \hline \end{array}$

6) $\begin{array}{r} 7,231 \\ +2,493 \\ \hline \end{array}$

✎ Find the missing numbers.

7) $1,998 + \underline{\hphantom{000}} = 3,451$

10) $748 + \underline{\hphantom{000}} = 2,950$

8) $700 + 3,000 = \underline{\hphantom{000}}$

11) $\underline{\hphantom{000}} + 956 = 3,783$

9) $2,500 + \underline{\hphantom{000}} = 3,880$

12) $\underline{\hphantom{000}} + 2,071 = 5,900$

13) David sells gems. He finds a diamond in Istanbul and buys it for $5,892. Then, he flies to Cairo and purchases a bigger diamond for the bargain price of $8,471. How much does David spend on the two diamonds?

Subtracting 4–Digit Numbers

✍ Subtract.

1) $\begin{array}{r} 7,343 \\ -\ 4,279 \\ \hline \end{array}$

4) $\begin{array}{r} 3,534 \\ -\ 1,956 \\ \hline \end{array}$

7) $\begin{array}{r} 2,369 \\ -\ 1,233 \\ \hline \end{array}$

2) $\begin{array}{r} 8,765 \\ -\ 4,453 \\ \hline \end{array}$

5) $\begin{array}{r} 9,142 \\ -\ 5,639 \\ \hline \end{array}$

8) $\begin{array}{r} 8,450 \\ -\ 6,169 \\ \hline \end{array}$

3) $\begin{array}{r} 6,475 \\ -\ 4,954 \\ \hline \end{array}$

6) $\begin{array}{r} 7,813 \\ -5,099 \\ \hline \end{array}$

9) $\begin{array}{r} 6,000 \\ -3,223 \\ \hline \end{array}$

✍ Find the missing number.

10) $5,632 - \rule{1cm}{0.15mm} = 2,953$

13) $6,700 - \rule{1cm}{0.15mm} = 4,968$

11) $4,572 - \rule{1cm}{0.15mm} = 3,132$

14) $3,752 - 2,542 = \rule{1cm}{0.15mm}$

12) $9,231 - 5,678 = \rule{1cm}{0.15mm}$

15) $4,887 - 3,762 = \rule{1cm}{0.15mm}$

16) Jackson had \$6,973 invested in the stock market until he lost \$2,784 on those investments. How much money does he have in the stock market now?

Answers of Worksheets – Chapter 2

Adding two–digit numbers

1) 96	6) 67	11) 80
2) 41	7) 82	12) 124
3) 88	8) 86	13) 104
4) 38	9) 90	14) 110
5) 100	10) 93	

Subtracting two–digit numbers

1) 11	6) 50	11) 15
2) 9	7) 23	12) 30
3) 13	8) 34	13) 24
4) 0	9) 31	14) 70
5) 35	10) 30	

Adding three–digit numbers

1) 437	6) 718	11) 1,138
2) 894	7) 757	12) 1,445
3) 1,098	8) 1,241	13) 1,262
4) 900	9) 1,029	14) 1,110
5) 240	10) 618	

Adding hundreds

1) 500	5) 1,100	9) 1,300	13) 600
2) 700	6) 1,200	10) 900	14) 1,000
3) 1,400	7) 1,700	11) 1,800	15) 1,600
4) 1,000	8) 1,600	12) 1,500	

Adding 4–digit numbers

1) 7,820	6) 9,724	11) 2,827
2) 9,149	7) 1,453	12) 3,829
3) 3,893	8) 3,700	13) $14,363
4) 9,823	9) 1,380	
5) 10,120	10) 2,202	

Subtracting 4–digit numbers

1. 3,064
2. 4,312
3. 1,521
4. 1,578
5. 3,503
6. 2,714

7. 1,136
8. 2,281
9. 2,777
10. 2,679
11. 1,440
12. 3,553

13. 1,732
14. 1,210
15. 1,125
16. 4,189

Chapter 3: Multiplication and Division

Topics that you'll practice in this chapter:

✓ Times Table

✓ Multiplication by 0 to 3

✓ Multiplication by 4 to 7

✓ Multiplication by 8 to 12

✓ Division by 0 to 6

✓ Division by 7 to 12

✓ Dividing by Tens

✓ Divide and Multiply 3–Digit Numbers by 1-digit Numbers

Multiplication by 0 to 3

✍ Write the answers.

1) $5 \times 2 =$ __

2) $5 \times 1 =$ __

3) $7 \times 2 =$ __

4) $7 \times 3 =$ __

5) $1 \times 6 =$ __

6) $2 \times 9 =$ __

7) $10 \times 2 =$ __

8) $1 \times 10 =$ __

9) $11 \times 1 =$ __

10) $5 \times 0 =$ __

11) $9 \times 3 =$ __

12) $11 \times 3 =$ __

13) $2 \times 8 =$ __

14) $3 \times 6 =$ __

15) $3 \times 3 =$ __

16) $8 \times 3 =$ __

✍ Find Each Missing Number.

17) $3 \times$ __ $= 24$

18) $6 \times$ __ $= 18$

19) $2 \times 4 =$ __

20) __ $\times 2 = 20$

21) __ $\times 3 = 36$

22) $7 \times$ __ $= 0$

23) $3 \times$ __ $= 15$

24) $9 \times$ __ $= 9$

25) $6 \times$ __ $= 12$

26) __ $\times 1 = 10$

27) __ $\times 5 = 10$

28) $9 \times 0 =$ __

29) $3 \times$ __ $= 30$

30) __ $\times 1 = 11$

Multiplication by 4 to 7

✍ Write the answers.

1) $7 \times 5 =$ ___

2) $5 \times 6 =$ ___

3) $10 \times 5 =$ ___

4) $12 \times 6 =$ ___

5) $9 \times 6 =$ ___

6) $11 \times 5 =$ ___

7) $8 \times 5 =$ ___

8) $7 \times 9 =$ ___

9) $20 \times 4 =$ ___

10) $4 \times 9 =$ ___

11) $11 \times 4 =$ ___

12) $9 \times 5 =$ ___

13) $8 \times 7 =$ ___

14) $12 \times 7 =$ ___

15) $8 \times 4 =$ ___

16) $5 \times 20 =$ ___

17) $7 \times 7 =$ ___

18) $6 \times 7 =$ ___

19) $4 \times 5 =$ ___

20) $4 \times 6 =$ ___

21) $4 \times 1 =$ ___

22) $7 \times 1 =$ ___

23) $6 \times 6 =$ ___

24) $4 \times 7 =$ ___

25) $10 \times 4 =$ ___

26) $12 \times 5 =$ ___

27) Ryan ordered six pizzas and sliced them into five pieces each. How many pieces of pizza were there?

_____

Multiplication by 8 to 12

✍ Write the answers.

1) $8 \times 8 =$ ___

2) $10 \times 8 =$ ___

3) $11 \times 10 =$ ___

4) $9 \times 12 =$ ___

5) $10 \times 10 =$ ___

6) $12 \times 11 =$ ___

7) $11 \times 7 =$ ___

8) $9 \times 8 =$ ___

9) $7 \times 12 =$ ___

10) $11 \times 9 =$ ___

11) $10 \times 7 =$ ___

12) $3 \times 12 =$ ___

13) $8 \times 11 =$ ___

14) $12 \times 12 =$ ___

15) $8 \times 6 =$ ___

16) $12 \times 1 =$ ___

17) $12 \times 4 =$ ___

18) $10 \times 9 =$ ___

19) $11 \times 9 =$ ___

20) $12 \times 3 =$ ___

21) $11 \times 2 =$ ___

22) $9 \times 8 =$ ___

23) There are 12 bananas in each box. How many bananas are in 8 boxes?

24) Each child has 8 apples. If there are 10 children, how many apples are there in total?

25) Each child has 10 pencils. If there are 13 children, how many pens are there in total?

Division by 0 to 6

✎ Find each missing number.

1) $60 \div \underline{\quad} = 12$

2) $32 \div 4 = \underline{\quad}$

3) $14 \div 2 = \underline{\quad}$

4) $35 \div 5 = \underline{\quad}$

5) $\underline{\quad} \div 2 = 11$

6) $10 \div 5 = \underline{\quad}$

7) $\underline{\quad} \div 2 = 8$

8) $15 \div \underline{\quad} = 5$

9) $\underline{\quad} \div 3 = 7$

10) $\underline{\quad} \div 4 = 6$

11) $\underline{\quad} \div 5 = 6$

12) $19 \div 1 = \underline{\quad}$

13) $6 \div \underline{\quad} = 3$

14) $22 \div 2 = \underline{\quad}$

15) $26 \div \underline{\quad} = 13$

16) $\underline{\quad} \div 4 = 9$

17) $30 \div 6 = \underline{\quad}$

18) $28 \div \underline{\quad} = 7$

19) $42 \div \underline{\quad} = 6$

20) $12 \div \underline{\quad} = 3$

21) $16 \div 2 = \underline{\quad}$

22) $10 \div 2 = \underline{\quad}$

23) $\underline{\quad} \div 1 = 9$

24) $27 \div \underline{\quad} = 9$

25) $40 \div 4 = \underline{\quad}$

26) $11 \div \underline{\quad} = 1$

27) $30 \div \underline{\quad} = 10$

28) $34 \div \underline{\quad} = 17$

29) $42 \div \underline{\quad} = 21$

30) $\underline{\quad} \div 5 = 12$

31) $48 \div 6 = \underline{\quad}$

32) $4 \div 2 = \underline{\quad}$

33) $\underline{\quad} \div 4 = 11$

34) $55 \div 5 = \underline{\quad}$

35) $51 \div 3 = \underline{\quad}$

36) $\underline{\quad} \div 5 = 9$

37) Mia has 30 strawberries that she would like to give to her 3 friends. If she shares them equally, how many strawberries will she give to each of her friends?

Division by 7 to 12

✏️ Find each missing number.

1) __ ÷ 13 = 1

2) __ ÷ 7 = 8

3) 90 ÷ 9 = __

4) 54 ÷ __ = 6

5) 81 ÷ 9 = __

6) __ ÷ 7 = 9

7) 42 ÷ __ = 6

8) __ ÷ 8 = 7

9) 36 ÷ __ = 4

10) 45 ÷ 9 = __

11) __ ÷ 10 = 10

12) 14 ÷ __ = 2

13) __ ÷ 12 = 9

14) 55 ÷ 11 = __

15) 110 ÷ __ = 10

16) 72 ÷ 8 = __

17) 96 ÷ 8 = __

18) 84 ÷ 7 = __

19) 80 ÷ __ = 10

20) 72 ÷ 12 = __

21) 36 ÷ __ = 3

22) 12 ÷ 12 = __

23) 147 ÷ __ = 21

24) 40 ÷ __ = 5

25) __ ÷ 8 = 11

26) 130 ÷ 10 = __

27) 121 ÷ __ = 11

28) 50 ÷ __ = 5

29) __ ÷ 12 = 2

30) __ ÷ 8 = 3

31) 18 ÷ __ = 2

32) __ ÷ 12 = 7

33) 54 ÷ 9 = __

34) 9 ÷ 9 = __

35) 45 ÷ 9 = __

36) 63 ÷ __ = 9

37) Stella has 64 fruit juice that she would like to give to her 8 friends. If she shares them equally, how many fruit juices will she give to each?

Dividing by Tens

✍ Find answers.

1) $600 \div 20 =$ ___

2) $300 \div 30 =$ ___

3) $1,400 \div 20 =$ ___

4) $450 \div 50 =$ ___

5) $320 \div 40 =$ ___

6) $100 \div 20 =$ ___

7) $360 \div 40 =$ ___

8) $210 \div 30 =$ ___

9) $1,500 \div 50 =$ ___

10) $220 \div 20 =$ ___

11) $770 \div 10 =$ ___

12) $180 \div 90 =$ ___

13) $260 \div 10 =$ ___

14) $540 \div 60 =$ ___

15) $160 \div 20 =$ ___

16) $510 \div 30 =$ ___

17) $200 \div 40 =$ ___

18) $400 \div 40 =$ ___

19) $\frac{420}{30} =$ ___

20) $\frac{800}{40} =$ ___

21) $\frac{700}{70} =$ ___

22) $\frac{660}{60} =$ ___

23) $\frac{280}{40} =$ ___

24) $\frac{350}{50} =$ ___

Divide and Multiply 3–Digit Numbers

✍ Find the answers.

1) $360 \div 6 =$ ____

2) $160 \div 8 =$ ____

3) $210 \div 7 =$ ____

4) $600 \div 6 =$ ____

5) $540 \div 6 =$ ____

6) $380 \div 2 =$ ____

7) $500 \div 5 =$ ____

8) $440 \div 4 =$ ____

9) $300 \div 3 =$ ____

10) $720 \div 9 =$ ____

11) $220 \div 2 =$ ____

12) $280 \div 4 =$ ____

13) $100 \div 5 =$ ____

14) $350 \div 5 =$ ____

15) $900 \div 3 =$ ____

16) $800 \div 8 =$ ____

17) $200 \div 8 =$ ____

18) $150 \div 3 =$ ____

19) $180 \div 6 =$ ____

20) $140 \div 7 =$ ____

✍ Find the answers.

21)
$$\begin{array}{r} 410 \\ \times\ 5 \\ \hline \end{array}$$

22)
$$\begin{array}{r} 140 \\ \times\ 6 \\ \hline \end{array}$$

23)
$$\begin{array}{r} 325 \\ \times\ 8 \\ \hline \end{array}$$

24)
$$\begin{array}{r} 260 \\ \times\ 4 \\ \hline \end{array}$$

25)
$$\begin{array}{r} 642 \\ \times\ 5 \\ \hline \end{array}$$

26)
$$\begin{array}{r} 423 \\ \times\ 7 \\ \hline \end{array}$$

27)
$$\begin{array}{r} 722 \\ \times\ 5 \\ \hline \end{array}$$

28)
$$\begin{array}{r} 112 \\ \times\ 6 \\ \hline \end{array}$$

29)
$$\begin{array}{r} 165 \\ \times\ 9 \\ \hline \end{array}$$

Times Table

×	1	2	3	4	5	6	7	8	9	10	11	12
1	1	2	3	4	5	6	7	8	9	10	11	12
2	2	4	6	8	10	12	14	16	18	20	22	24
3	3	6	9	12	15	18	21	24	27	30	33	36
4	4	8	12	16	20	24	28	32	36	40	44	48
5	5	10	15	20	25	30	35	40	45	50	55	60
6	6	12	18	24	30	36	42	48	54	60	66	72
7	7	14	21	28	35	42	49	56	63	70	77	84
8	8	16	24	32	40	48	56	64	72	80	88	96
9	9	18	27	36	45	54	63	72	81	90	99	108
10	10	20	30	40	50	60	70	80	90	100	110	120
11	11	22	33	44	55	66	77	88	99	110	121	132
12	12	24	36	48	60	72	84	96	108	120	132	144

Answers of Worksheets – Chapter 3

Multiplication by 0 to 3

1) 10	11) 27	21) 12
2) 5	12) 33	22) 0
3) 14	13) 16	23) 5
4) 21	14) 18	24) 1
5) 6	15) 9	25) 2
6) 18	16) 24	26) 10
7) 20	17) 8	27) 2
8) 10	18) 3	28) 0
9) 11	19) 8	29) 10
10) 0	20) 10	30) 11

Multiplication by 4 to 7

1) 35	10) 36	19) 20
2) 30	11) 44	20) 24
3) 50	12) 45	21) 4
4) 72	13) 56	22) 7
5) 54	14) 84	23) 36
6) 55	15) 32	24) 28
7) 40	16) 100	25) 40
8) 63	17) 49	26) 60
9) 80	18) 42	27) 30

Multiplication by 8 to 12

1) 64	7) 77	13) 88
2) 80	8) 72	14) 144
3) 110	9) 84	15) 48
4) 108	10) 99	16) 12
5) 100	11) 70	17) 48
6) 132	12) 36	18) 90

19) 99

20) 36

21) 22

22) 72

23) 96

24) 80

25) 130

Division by 0 to 6

1) 4

2) 8

3) 7

4) 7

5) 22

6) 2

7) 16

8) 3

9) 21

10) 24

11) 30

12) 19

13) 2

14) 11

15) 2

16) 36

17) 5

18) 4

19) 7

20) 4

21) 8

22) 5

23) 9

24) 3

25) 10

26) 11

27) 3

28) 2

29) 2

30) 60

31) 8

32) 2

33) 44

34) 11

35) 17

36) 45

37) 10

Division by 7 to 12

1) 13

2) 56

3) 10

4) 9

5) 9

6) 63

7) 7

8) 56

9) 9

10) 5

11) 100

12) 7

13) 108

14) 5

15) 11

16) 9

17) 12

18) 12

19) 8

20) 6

21) 12

22) 1

23) 7

24) 8

25) 88

26) 13

27) 11

28) 10

29) 24

30) 24

31) 9

32) 84

33) 6

34) 1

35) 5

36) 7

37) 8

Dividing by tens

1) 30
2) 10
3) 70
4) 9
5) 8
6) 5
7) 9
8) 7

9) 30
10) 11
11) 77
12) 2
13) 26
14) 9
15) 8
16) 17

17) 5
18) 10
19) 14
20) 20
21) 10
22) 11
23) 7
24) 7

Divide and Multiply 3-digit numbers by 1-digit numbers

1) 60
2) 20
3) 30
4) 100
5) 90
6) 160
7) 100
8) 110
9) 100
10) 80

11) 110
12) 70
13) 20
14) 70
15) 300
16) 100
17) 40
18) 50
19) 30
20) 20

21) 2,050
22) 840
23) 2,600
24) 1,040
25) 3,210
26) 2,961
27) 3,610
28) 672
29) 1,485

Chapter 4: Fractions

Topics that you'll learn in this chapter:

- ✓ Fractions of a Number
- ✓ Order Fractions
- ✓ Simplifying Fractions
- ✓ Improper Fractions
- ✓ Comparing Fractions
- ✓ Add Fractions
- ✓ Subtract Fractions
- ✓ Compare Sums and Differences of Fractions
- ✓ Add 3 or More Fractions

Fractions of a Number

✐ Solve.

1) Find $\frac{1}{3}$ of 90.

2) Find $\frac{5}{6}$ of 120.

3) Find $\frac{1}{5}$ of 80.

4) Find $\frac{1}{2}$ of 70.

5) Find $\frac{1}{2}$ of 50.

6) Find $\frac{2}{3}$ of 60.

7) Find $\frac{1}{4}$ of 64.

8) Find $\frac{3}{2}$ of 20.

9) Find $\frac{2}{5}$ of 55.

10) Find $\frac{2}{9}$ of 81.

11) Find $\frac{3}{7}$ of 49.

12) Find $\frac{1}{6}$ of 48.

13) Find $\frac{3}{8}$ of 80.

14) Find $\frac{1}{4}$ of 52.

15) Find $\frac{5}{7}$ of 56.

16) Find $\frac{2}{5}$ of 125.

17) Find $\frac{3}{8}$ of 152.

18) Find $\frac{3}{4}$ of 400.

19) Find $\frac{2}{9}$ of 180.

20) Find $\frac{1}{40}$ of 160.

Order Fractions

✎ Order the fractions from greatest to latest.

1) $\frac{1}{5}, \frac{2}{5}, \frac{1}{10}$

2) $\frac{1}{4}, \frac{3}{2}, \frac{5}{8}$

3) $\frac{5}{12}, \frac{5}{6}, \frac{1}{4}$

4) $\frac{1}{4}, \frac{3}{8}, \frac{5}{16}$

5) $\frac{1}{6}, \frac{2}{3}, \frac{5}{18}$

6) $\frac{1}{6}, \frac{2}{3}, \frac{2}{6}$

7) $\frac{1}{3}, \frac{3}{5}, \frac{6}{15}$

8) $\frac{2}{7}, \frac{3}{14}, \frac{4}{7}$

9) $\frac{6}{5}, \frac{1}{5}, \frac{2}{15}$

10) $\frac{3}{7}, \frac{5}{7}, \frac{4}{7}$

✎ Order the fractions from latest to greatest.

11) $\frac{5}{6}, \frac{9}{6}, \frac{3}{6}$

12) $\frac{3}{8}, \frac{6}{8}, \frac{2}{8}$

13) $\frac{4}{9}, \frac{2}{5}, \frac{7}{9}$

14) $\frac{3}{2}, \frac{1}{2}, \frac{2}{2}$

15) $\frac{4}{9}, \frac{7}{9}, \frac{2}{9}$

16) $\frac{3}{8}, \frac{4}{4}, \frac{2}{4}$

17) $\frac{1}{4}, \frac{5}{6}, \frac{4}{6}$

18) $\frac{10}{5}, \frac{20}{5}, \frac{9}{5}$

Simplifying Fractions

✎ Simplify each fraction to its lowest terms.

1) $\frac{16}{32} =$

2) $\frac{12}{15} =$

3) $\frac{27}{36} =$

4) $\frac{20}{80} =$

5) $\frac{39}{52} =$

6) $\frac{22}{33} =$

7) $\frac{28}{35} =$

8) $\frac{5}{20} =$

9) $\frac{27}{54} =$

10) $\frac{16}{24} =$

11) $\frac{25}{75} =$

12) $\frac{45}{60} =$

13) $\frac{81}{99} =$

14) $\frac{117}{130} =$

15) $\frac{15}{20} =$

16) $\frac{25}{105} =$

17) $\frac{80}{192} =$

18) $\frac{60}{100} =$

19) $\frac{72}{153} =$

20) $\frac{120}{520} =$

21) $\frac{360}{720} =$

✎ Solve each problem.

22) Which of the following fractions equal to $\frac{5}{7}$? _____

   A. $\frac{20}{49}$ B. $\frac{40}{56}$ C. $\frac{40}{49}$ D. $\frac{35}{56}$

23) Which of the following fractions equal to $\frac{3}{5}$? _____

   A. $\frac{54}{90}$ B. $\frac{30}{200}$ C. $\frac{39}{60}$ D. $\frac{28}{80}$

24) Which of the following fractions equal to $\frac{7}{8}$? _____

   A. $\frac{72}{99}$ B. $\frac{133}{152}$ C. $\frac{125}{133}$ D. $\frac{136}{512}$

Improper Fractions

✍ Fill in the blank.

1) $\dfrac{5}{3} + \underline{} = 2$

2) $\dfrac{9}{5} + \underline{} = 6$

3) $\dfrac{1}{4} + \underline{} = 2$

4) $\dfrac{5}{3} + \underline{} = 3$

5) $\dfrac{2}{5} + \underline{} = 1$

6) $\dfrac{1}{6} + \underline{} = 1$

7) $\dfrac{3}{4} + \underline{} = 2$

8) $\dfrac{2}{3} + \underline{} = 3$

9) $\dfrac{5}{8} + \underline{} = 3$

10) $\dfrac{2}{3} + \underline{} = 4$

✍ Convert Improper fractions to mixed numbers.

11) $\dfrac{6}{5} =$

12) $\dfrac{8}{3} =$

13) $\dfrac{5}{3} =$

14) $\dfrac{11}{4} =$

15) $\dfrac{9}{5} =$

16) $\dfrac{14}{5} =$

17) $\dfrac{9}{2} =$

18) $\dfrac{13}{3} =$

19) $\dfrac{11}{9} =$

20) $\dfrac{15}{7} =$

Comparing Fractions

✎ Use > = < to compare fractions.

1) $\dfrac{1}{4} \square \dfrac{4}{8}$

2) $\dfrac{3}{30} \square \dfrac{1}{5}$

3) $\dfrac{11}{45} \square \dfrac{2}{15}$

4) $\dfrac{9}{21} \square \dfrac{3}{7}$

5) $\dfrac{9}{54} \square \dfrac{1}{6}$

6) $\dfrac{16}{32} \square \dfrac{7}{8}$

7) $\dfrac{8}{14} \square \dfrac{16}{28}$

8) $\dfrac{33}{44} \square \dfrac{40}{44}$

✎ Find the missing values.

9) $\dfrac{1}{5} = \dfrac{}{30}$

10) $\dfrac{}{7} = \dfrac{7}{49}$

11) $\dfrac{}{12} = \dfrac{1}{4}$

12) $\dfrac{5}{15} = \dfrac{1}{}$

13) $\dfrac{}{11} = \dfrac{40}{88}$

14) $\dfrac{7}{63} = \dfrac{}{9}$

15) $\dfrac{5}{13} = \dfrac{10}{}$

16) $\dfrac{8}{9} = \dfrac{24}{}$

17) $\dfrac{6}{36} = \dfrac{}{6}$

18) $\dfrac{7}{35} = \dfrac{}{5}$

Add Fractions

✎ Add fractions.

1) $\dfrac{4}{9} + \dfrac{5}{9} =$

2) $\dfrac{5}{12} + \dfrac{7}{12} =$

3) $\dfrac{7}{15} + \dfrac{4}{15} =$

4) $\dfrac{7}{3} + \dfrac{8}{3} =$

5) $\dfrac{7}{16} + \dfrac{4}{16} =$

6) $\dfrac{5}{9} + \dfrac{2}{9} =$

7) $\dfrac{6}{4} + \dfrac{5}{4} =$

8) $\dfrac{3}{15} + \dfrac{8}{15} =$

9) $\dfrac{7}{23} + \dfrac{9}{23} =$

10) $\dfrac{4}{6} + \dfrac{1}{6} =$

11) $\dfrac{7}{26} + \dfrac{9}{26} =$

12) $\dfrac{3}{11} + \dfrac{5}{11} =$

13) $\dfrac{7}{17} + \dfrac{10}{17} =$

14) $\dfrac{14}{29} + \dfrac{2}{29} =$

15) $\dfrac{9}{31} + \dfrac{2}{31} =$

16) $\dfrac{10}{34} + \dfrac{3}{34} =$

17) $\dfrac{3}{28} + \dfrac{8}{28} =$

18) $\dfrac{8}{41} + \dfrac{13}{41} =$

19) $\dfrac{17}{33} + \dfrac{8}{33} =$

20) $\dfrac{3}{49} + \dfrac{5}{49} =$

21) $\dfrac{21}{51} + \dfrac{10}{51} =$

22) $\dfrac{12}{55} + \dfrac{9}{55} =$

Subtract Fractions

✎ Subtract fractions.

1) $\dfrac{5}{6} - \dfrac{4}{6} =$

2) $\dfrac{3}{8} - \dfrac{2}{8} =$

3) $\dfrac{15}{17} - \dfrac{9}{17} =$

4) $\dfrac{9}{10} - \dfrac{6}{10} =$

5) $\dfrac{7}{11} - \dfrac{4}{11} =$

6) $\dfrac{6}{14} - \dfrac{5}{14} =$

7) $\dfrac{12}{19} - \dfrac{9}{19} =$

8) $\dfrac{15}{16} - \dfrac{12}{16} =$

9) $\dfrac{18}{23} - \dfrac{8}{23} =$

10) $\dfrac{9}{28} - \dfrac{4}{28} =$

11) $\dfrac{25}{33} - \dfrac{15}{33} =$

12) $\dfrac{11}{26} - \dfrac{10}{26} =$

13) $\dfrac{12}{29} - \dfrac{8}{29} =$

14) $\dfrac{15}{30} - \dfrac{14}{30} =$

15) $\dfrac{20}{22} - \dfrac{19}{22} =$

16) $\dfrac{16}{50} - \dfrac{13}{50} =$

17) $\dfrac{33}{43} - \dfrac{22}{43} =$

18) $\dfrac{17}{52} - \dfrac{10}{52} =$

19) $\dfrac{34}{80} - \dfrac{17}{80} =$

20) $\dfrac{39}{65} - \dfrac{20}{65} =$

21) $\dfrac{11}{81} - \dfrac{9}{81} =$

22) $\dfrac{25}{88} - \dfrac{22}{88} =$

Add and Subtract Fractions

✎ Add fractions.

1) $\dfrac{5}{8} + \dfrac{3}{8} =$

2) $\dfrac{3}{10} + \dfrac{7}{10} =$

3) $\dfrac{5}{11} + \dfrac{3}{11} =$

4) $\dfrac{3}{13} + \dfrac{4}{13} =$

5) $\dfrac{9}{17} + \dfrac{2}{17} =$

6) $\dfrac{3}{16} + \dfrac{1}{16} =$

7) $\dfrac{1}{19} + \dfrac{4}{19} =$

8) $\dfrac{18}{21} + \dfrac{3}{21} =$

9) $\dfrac{1}{36} + \dfrac{2}{36} =$

10) $\dfrac{11}{27} + \dfrac{10}{27} =$

✎ Subtract fractions.

11) $\dfrac{5}{9} - \dfrac{3}{9} =$

12) $\dfrac{9}{12} - \dfrac{8}{12} =$

13) $\dfrac{4}{14} - \dfrac{3}{14} =$

14) $\dfrac{11}{15} - \dfrac{4}{15} =$

15) $\dfrac{8}{21} - \dfrac{3}{21} =$

16) $\dfrac{7}{23} - \dfrac{5}{23} =$

17) $\dfrac{25}{43} - \dfrac{23}{43} =$

18) $\dfrac{28}{45} - \dfrac{26}{45} =$

19) $\dfrac{15}{51} - \dfrac{13}{51} =$

20) $\dfrac{22}{83} - \dfrac{17}{83} =$

Compare Sums and Differences of Fractions

✎ Evaluate and compare. Write < or > or =.

1) $\dfrac{2}{5} + \dfrac{3}{5} \;\square\; \dfrac{1}{5}$

2) $\dfrac{3}{4} + \dfrac{1}{4} \;\square\; 1$

3) $\dfrac{3}{9} + \dfrac{2}{9} \;\square\; \dfrac{5}{9}$

4) $\dfrac{2}{5} + \dfrac{1}{5} \;\square\; \dfrac{1}{5}$

5) $\dfrac{7}{11} + \dfrac{4}{11} \;\square\; \dfrac{1}{11}$

6) $\dfrac{8}{9} - \dfrac{4}{9} \;\square\; \dfrac{5}{9}$

7) $\dfrac{3}{16} + \dfrac{6}{16} \;\square\; \dfrac{6}{16}$

8) $\dfrac{9}{19} - \dfrac{7}{19} \;\square\; \dfrac{8}{19}$

9) $\dfrac{11}{17} - \dfrac{4}{17} \;\square\; \dfrac{5}{17}$

10) $\dfrac{2}{4} + \dfrac{1}{4} \;\square\; \dfrac{1}{4}$

11) $\dfrac{7}{13} + \dfrac{3}{13} \;\square\; \dfrac{8}{13}$

12) $\dfrac{15}{12} - \dfrac{10}{12} \;\square\; \dfrac{11}{12}$

13) $\dfrac{3}{10} + \dfrac{7}{10} \;\square\; \dfrac{8}{10}$

14) $\dfrac{13}{14} - \dfrac{8}{14} \;\square\; \dfrac{11}{14}$

15) $\dfrac{20}{22} - \dfrac{19}{22} \;\square\; \dfrac{11}{22}$

16) $\dfrac{16}{30} + \dfrac{14}{30} \;\square\; \dfrac{19}{30}$

17) $\dfrac{20}{33} - \dfrac{13}{33} \;\square\; \dfrac{5}{33}$

18) $\dfrac{45}{47} - \dfrac{15}{47} \;\square\; \dfrac{35}{47}$

19) $\dfrac{9}{32} + \dfrac{6}{32} \;\square\; \dfrac{7}{32}$

20) $\dfrac{21}{53} + \dfrac{10}{53} \;\square\; \dfrac{25}{53}$

Add 3 or More Fractions

✎ Add fractions.

1) $\dfrac{3}{7} + \dfrac{2}{7} + \dfrac{2}{7} =$

12) $\dfrac{5}{33} + \dfrac{16}{33} + \dfrac{5}{33} =$

2) $\dfrac{2}{10} + \dfrac{2}{10} + \dfrac{3}{10} =$

13) $\dfrac{7}{30} + \dfrac{5}{30} + \dfrac{1}{30} =$

3) $\dfrac{1}{13} + \dfrac{4}{13} + \dfrac{1}{13} =$

14) $\dfrac{4}{39} + \dfrac{1}{39} + \dfrac{8}{39} =$

4) $\dfrac{4}{14} + \dfrac{7}{14} + \dfrac{3}{14} =$

15) $\dfrac{2}{43} + \dfrac{6}{43} + \dfrac{7}{43} =$

5) $\dfrac{2}{6} + \dfrac{3}{6} + \dfrac{1}{6} =$

16) $\dfrac{11}{50} + \dfrac{8}{50} + \dfrac{15}{50} =$

6) $\dfrac{1}{16} + \dfrac{6}{16} + \dfrac{3}{16} =$

17) $\dfrac{9}{37} + \dfrac{3}{37} + \dfrac{4}{37} =$

7) $\dfrac{1}{3} + \dfrac{2}{3} + \dfrac{1}{3} =$

18) $\dfrac{2}{41} + \dfrac{3}{41} + \dfrac{9}{41} =$

8) $\dfrac{7}{18} + \dfrac{3}{18} + \dfrac{7}{18} =$

19) $\dfrac{5}{48} + \dfrac{4}{48} + \dfrac{10}{48} =$

9) $\dfrac{4}{20} + \dfrac{1}{20} + \dfrac{2}{20} =$

20) $\dfrac{9}{72} + \dfrac{16}{72} + \dfrac{11}{72} =$

10) $\dfrac{5}{22} + \dfrac{2}{22} + \dfrac{2}{22} =$

21) $\dfrac{13}{49} + \dfrac{13}{49} + \dfrac{8}{49} =$

11) $\dfrac{11}{29} + \dfrac{2}{29} + \dfrac{1}{29} =$

22) $\dfrac{25}{90} + \dfrac{17}{90} + \dfrac{8}{90} =$

Answers of Worksheets – Chapter 4

Fractions of a number

1) 30

2) 100

3) 16

4) 35

5) 25

6) 40

7) 16

8) 30

9) 22

10) 18

11) 21

12) 8

13) 30

14) 13

15) 40

16) 50

17) 57

18) 300

19) 40

20) 4

Order fractions

1) $\frac{2}{5}, \frac{1}{5}, \frac{1}{10}$

2) $\frac{3}{2}, \frac{5}{8}, \frac{1}{4}$

3) $\frac{5}{6}, \frac{5}{12}, \frac{1}{4}$

4) $\frac{3}{8}, \frac{5}{16}, \frac{1}{4}$

5) $\frac{2}{3}, \frac{5}{18}, \frac{1}{6}$

6) $\frac{2}{3}, \frac{2}{6}, \frac{1}{6}$

7) $\frac{3}{5}, \frac{6}{15}, \frac{1}{3}$

8) $\frac{4}{7}, \frac{2}{7}, \frac{3}{14}$

9) $\frac{6}{5}, \frac{1}{5}, \frac{2}{15}$

10) $\frac{5}{7}, \frac{4}{7}, \frac{3}{7}$

11) $\frac{3}{6}, \frac{5}{6}, \frac{9}{6}$

12) $\frac{2}{8}, \frac{3}{8}, \frac{6}{8}$

13) $\frac{2}{5}, \frac{4}{9}, \frac{7}{9}$

14) $\frac{1}{2}, \frac{2}{2}, \frac{3}{2}$

15) $\frac{2}{9}, \frac{4}{9}, \frac{7}{9}$

16) $\frac{3}{8}, \frac{2}{4}, \frac{4}{4}$

17) $\frac{1}{4}, \frac{4}{6}, \frac{5}{6}$

18) $\frac{9}{5}, \frac{10}{5}, \frac{20}{5}$

Simplifying Fractions

1) $\frac{1}{2}$

2) $\frac{4}{5}$

3) $\frac{3}{4}$

4) $\frac{1}{4}$

5) $\frac{3}{4}$

6) $\frac{2}{3}$

7) $\frac{4}{5}$

8) $\frac{1}{4}$

9) $\frac{1}{2}$

10) $\frac{2}{3}$

11) $\frac{1}{3}$

12) $\frac{3}{4}$

13) $\frac{9}{11}$

14) $\frac{9}{10}$

15) $\frac{3}{4}$

16) $\frac{5}{21}$

17) $\frac{5}{12}$

18) $\frac{3}{5}$

19) $\frac{8}{17}$

20) $\frac{3}{13}$

21) $\frac{1}{2}$

22) B

23) A

24) B

Improper Fraction

1) $\frac{1}{3}$

2) $\frac{21}{5}$

3) $\frac{7}{4}$

4) $\frac{4}{3}$

5) $\frac{3}{5}$

6) $\frac{5}{6}$

7) $\frac{5}{4}$

8) $\frac{7}{3}$

9) $\frac{19}{8}$

10) $\frac{10}{3}$

11) $1\frac{1}{5}$

12) $2\frac{2}{3}$

13) $1\frac{2}{3}$

14) $2\frac{3}{4}$

15) $1\frac{4}{5}$

16) $2\frac{4}{5}$

17) $4\frac{1}{2}$

18) $4\frac{1}{3}$

19) $1\frac{2}{9}$

20) $2\frac{1}{7}$

Comparing Fractions and Missing Denominator

1) $\frac{1}{4} = \frac{4}{8}$

2) $\frac{3}{30} < \frac{1}{5}$

3) $\frac{11}{45} > \frac{2}{15}$

4) $\frac{9}{21} = \frac{3}{7}$

5) $\frac{9}{54} = \frac{1}{6}$

6) $\frac{16}{32} < \frac{7}{8}$

7) $\frac{8}{14} = \frac{16}{28}$

8) $\frac{33}{44} < \frac{40}{44}$

9) $\frac{1}{5} = \frac{6}{30}$

10) $\frac{1}{7} = \frac{7}{49}$

11) $\frac{3}{12} = \frac{1}{4}$

12) $\frac{5}{15} = \frac{1}{3}$

13) $\frac{5}{11} = \frac{40}{88}$

14) $\frac{7}{63} = \frac{1}{9}$

15) $\frac{5}{13} = \frac{10}{26}$

16) $\frac{8}{9} = \frac{24}{27}$

17) $\frac{6}{36} = \frac{1}{6}$

18) $\frac{7}{35} = \frac{1}{5}$

Add Fractions

1) 1

2) 1

3) $\frac{11}{15}$

4) 5

5) $\frac{11}{16}$

6) $\frac{7}{9}$

7) $\frac{11}{4}$

8) $\frac{11}{15}$

9) $\frac{16}{23}$

10) $\frac{5}{6}$

11) $\frac{16}{26}$

12) $\frac{8}{11}$

13) 1

14) $\frac{16}{29}$

15) $\frac{11}{31}$

16) $\frac{13}{34}$

17) $\frac{11}{28}$

18) $\frac{21}{41}$

19) $\frac{25}{33}$

20) $\frac{8}{49}$

21) $\frac{31}{51}$

22) $\frac{21}{55}$

Subtract Fractions

1) $\frac{1}{6}$

2) $\frac{1}{8}$

3) $\frac{6}{17}$

4) $\frac{3}{10}$

5) $\frac{3}{11}$

6) $\frac{1}{14}$

7) $\frac{7}{19}$

8) $\frac{3}{16}$

9) $\frac{10}{23}$

10) $\frac{5}{28}$

11) $\frac{10}{33}$

12) $\frac{1}{26}$

13) $\frac{4}{29}$

14) $\frac{1}{30}$

15) $\frac{1}{22}$

16) $\frac{3}{50}$

17) $\frac{11}{43}$ 19) $\frac{17}{80}$ 21) $\frac{2}{81}$

18) $\frac{7}{52}$ 20) $\frac{19}{65}$ 22) $\frac{3}{88}$

Add and Subtract Fractions

1) 1

2) 1

3) $\frac{8}{11}$

4) $\frac{7}{13}$

5) $\frac{11}{17}$

6) $\frac{1}{4}$

7) $\frac{5}{19}$

8) 1

9) $\frac{1}{12}$

10) $\frac{21}{27}$

11) $\frac{2}{9}$

12) $\frac{1}{12}$

13) $\frac{1}{14}$

14) $\frac{7}{15}$

15) $\frac{5}{21}$

16) $\frac{2}{23}$

17) $\frac{2}{43}$

18) $\frac{2}{45}$

19) $\frac{2}{51}$

20) $\frac{5}{83}$

Compare Sums and Differences of Fractions

1) $1 > \frac{1}{5}$

2) $1 = 1$

3) $\frac{5}{9} = \frac{5}{9}$

4) $\frac{3}{5} > \frac{1}{5}$

5) $1 > \frac{1}{11}$

6) $\frac{4}{9} < \frac{5}{9}$

7) $\frac{9}{16} > \frac{6}{16}$

8) $\frac{2}{19} < \frac{8}{19}$

9) $\frac{7}{17} > \frac{5}{17}$

10) $\frac{3}{4} > \frac{1}{4}$

11) $\frac{10}{13} > \frac{8}{13}$

12) $\frac{5}{12} < \frac{11}{12}$

13) $1 > \frac{8}{10}$

14) $\frac{5}{14} < \frac{11}{14}$

15) $\frac{1}{22} < \frac{11}{22}$

16) $1 > \frac{19}{30}$

17) $\frac{7}{33} > \frac{5}{33}$

18) $\frac{30}{47} < \frac{35}{47}$

19) $\frac{15}{32} > \frac{7}{32}$

20) $\frac{31}{53} > \frac{25}{53}$

Add 3 or More Fractions

1) 1

2) $\frac{7}{10}$

3) $\frac{6}{13}$

4) 1

5) 1

6) $\frac{10}{16}$

7) $\frac{4}{3}$

8) $\frac{17}{18}$

9) $\frac{7}{20}$

10) $\frac{9}{22}$

11) $\frac{14}{29}$

12) $\frac{26}{33}$

13) $\frac{13}{30}$

14) $\frac{13}{39}$

15) $\frac{15}{43}$

16) $\frac{34}{50}$

17) $\frac{16}{37}$

18) $\frac{14}{41}$

19) $\frac{19}{48}$

20) $\frac{36}{72}$

21) $\frac{34}{49}$

22) $\frac{50}{90}$

Chapter 5: Time and Money

Topics that you'll learn in this chapter:

- ✓ Read Clocks

- ✓ Telling Time

- ✓ Electronic Clock

- ✓ Measurement – Time

- ✓ Calendars

- ✓ Money Amounts

- ✓ Money: Word Problems

Read Clocks

✎ Write the time below each clock.

1)

_____

2)

_____

3)

_____

4)

_____

5)

_____

6)

_____

Telling Time

1) What time is shown by this clock?

_____

2) It is night. What time is shown on this clock?

_____

✍ Draw the hands on the clock face.

3)

.......05:10.......

4)

.......09:25.......

5)

.......06:50.......

6)

.......07:55.......

Digital Clock

What time is it? Write the time in words in front of each.

1) 5: 45   _____

2) 6: 30   _____

3) 9: 15   _____

4) 7: 25   _____

5) 3: 35   _____

6) 11: 05   _____

7) 4: 15   _____

8) 2: 20   _____

Measurement – Time

✍ How much time has passed?

1) 2:25 AM to 6:45 AM: _____ hours and _____ minutes.

2) 1:10 AM to 6:15 AM: _____ hours and _____ minutes.

3) 5:00 AM. to 6:15 AM. = _____ hour(s) and _____ minutes.

4) 7:10 PM to 9:25 PM. = _____ hour(s) and _____ minutes

5) 8:15 A.M. to 8:45 A.M. = _____ minutes

6) 6:25 A.M. to 6:50 A.M. = _____ minutes

7) There are _____ second in 15 minutes.

8) There are _____ second in 17 minutes.

9) There are _____ second in 22 minutes.

10) There are _____ minutes in 30 hours.

11) There are _____ minutes in 8 hours.

12) There are _____ minutes in 11 hours

13) There are _____ minutes in 35 hours

14) There are _____ minutes in 13 hours.

Calendars

February						
Sun	Mon	Tue	Wed	Thu	Fri	Sat
			1	2	3	4
5	6	7	8	9	10	11
12	13	14	15	16	17	18
19	20	21	22	23	24	25
26	27	28				

1. How many Friday are in the calendar?

   _____

2. What is the day on the 6th of February?

   _____

3. What is the date in the second Sunday of the month?

   _____

Money Amounts

Add.

1)
$$\begin{array}{r} \$458 \\ +\$184 \\ \hline \end{array}$$
$$\begin{array}{r} \$654 \\ +\$280 \\ \hline \end{array}$$
$$\begin{array}{r} \$586 \\ +\$315 \\ \hline \end{array}$$

2)
$$\begin{array}{r} \$357 \\ +\$378 \\ \hline \end{array}$$
$$\begin{array}{r} \$615 \\ +\$299 \\ \hline \end{array}$$
$$\begin{array}{r} \$645 \\ +\$214 \\ \hline \end{array}$$

3)
$$\begin{array}{r} \$575 \\ +\$298 \\ \hline \end{array}$$
$$\begin{array}{r} \$741 \\ +\$280 \\ \hline \end{array}$$
$$\begin{array}{r} \$758 \\ +\$288 \\ \hline \end{array}$$

4)
$$\begin{array}{r} \$925 \\ +\$215 \\ \hline \end{array}$$
$$\begin{array}{r} \$610 \\ +\$112 \\ \hline \end{array}$$
$$\begin{array}{r} \$780 \\ +\$420 \\ \hline \end{array}$$

Subtract.

1)
$$\begin{array}{r} \$845 \\ -\$259 \\ \hline \end{array}$$
$$\begin{array}{r} \$815 \\ -\$198 \\ \hline \end{array}$$
$$\begin{array}{r} \$548 \\ -\$218 \\ \hline \end{array}$$

2)
$$\begin{array}{r} \$685 \\ -\$325 \\ \hline \end{array}$$
$$\begin{array}{r} \$559 \\ -\$259 \\ \hline \end{array}$$
$$\begin{array}{r} \$869 \\ -\$750 \\ \hline \end{array}$$

3)
$$\begin{array}{r} \$390 \\ -\$121 \\ \hline \end{array}$$
$$\begin{array}{r} \$645 \\ -\$254 \\ \hline \end{array}$$
$$\begin{array}{r} \$785 \\ -\$625 \\ \hline \end{array}$$

4) Linda had $17.70. She bought some game tickets for $8.10. How much did she have left?

Money: Word Problems

✍Solve.

1) How many boxes of envelopes can you buy with $30 if one box costs $6?

2) After paying $6.35 for a salad, Ella has $50.36. How much money did she have before buying the salad?

3) How many packages of diapers can you buy with $90 if one package costs $9?

4) Last week James ran 42 miles more than Michael. James ran 87 miles. How many miles did Michael run?

5) Last Friday Jacob had $27.83. Over the weekend he received some money for cleaning the attic. He now has $68. How much money did he receive?

6) After paying $14.17 for a sandwich, Amelia has $29.52. How much money did she have before buying the sandwich?

Answers of Worksheets – Chapter 5

Read clocks

1) 4: 00

2) 10: 30

3) 7: 15

4) 1: 35

5) 5: 45

6) 8: 15

Telling Time

1) 7:50

2) 6:00

3)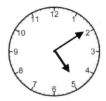

4)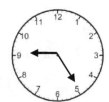

5)

6)

Digital Clock

1) It's five forty–five.

2) It's six thirty.

3) It's nine Fifteen.

4) It's seven twenty- five.

5) It's three thirty-five.

6) It's eleven five.

7) It's four Fifteen.

8) It's two twenty.

Measurement – Time

1) 4:20

2) 5:05

3) 1:15

4) 2:15

5) 30 minutes

6) 25 minutes

7) 900

8) 1,020

9) 1,320

10) 1,800

11) 480

12) 660

13) 2,100

14) 780

Calendars

1) 4

2) Monday

3) 12th

Add Money Amounts

1) 642; 934; 901

2) 735; 914; 859

3) 873; 1,021; 1,046

4) 1,140; 722; 1,200

Subtract Money Amounts

1) 586; 617; 330

2) 360; 300; 119

3) 269; 391; 160

4) 9.60

Money: word problem

1) 5

2) $56.71

3) 10

4) 45

5) 40.17

6) 15.35

Chapter 6: Measurement

Topics that you'll learn in this chapter:

- ✓ Reference Measurement

- ✓ Metric Length

- ✓ Customary Length

- ✓ Metric Capacity

- ✓ Customary Capacity

- ✓ Metric Weight and Mass

- ✓ Customary Weight and Mass

Reference Measurement

LENGTH

Customary	Metric
1 mile (mi) = 1,760 yards (yd)	1 kilometer (km) = 1,000 meters (m)
1 yard (yd) = 3 feet (ft)	1 meter (m) = 100 centimeters (cm)
1 foot (ft) = 12 inches (in.)	1 centimeter(cm)= 10 millimeters(mm)

VOLUME AND CAPACITY

Customary	Metric
1 gallon (gal) = 4 quarts (qt)	1 liter (L) = 1,000 milliliters (mL)
1 quart (qt) = 2 pints (pt.)	
1 pint (pt.) = 2 cups (c)	
1 cup (c) = 8 fluid ounces (Fl oz)	

WEIGHT AND MASS

Customary	Metric
1 ton (T) = 2,000 pounds (lb.)	1 kilogram (kg) = 1,000 grams (g)
1 pound (lb.) = 16 ounces (oz)	1 gram (g) = 1,000 milligrams (mg)

Time

1 year = 12 months

1 year = 52 weeks

1 week = 7 days

1 day = 24 hours

1 hour = 60 minutes

1 minute = 60 seconds

Metric Length Measurement

✍ Convert to the units.

1) 300 mm = _____ cm

2) 8 m = _____ mm

3) 5 m = _____ cm

4) 7 km = _____ m

5) 9,000 mm = _____ m

6) 1,000 cm = _____ m

7) 2 m = _____ cm

8) 4,000 mm = _____ cm

9) 7,000 mm = _____ m

10) 2 km = _____ m

11) 5 km = _____ m

12) 20 m = _____ cm

13) 5,000 m = _____ km

14) 7,000 m = _____ km

Customary Length Measurement

✍ Convert to the units.

1) 8 ft = _____ in

2) 4 ft = _____ in

3) 6 yd = _____ ft

4) 15 yd = _____ ft

5) 1,760 yd = _____ mi

6) 60 in = _____ ft

7) 144 in = _____ yd

8) 24 yd = _____ ft

9) 2 yd = _____ in

10) 5 yd = _____ in

11) 99 ft = _____ yd

12) 60 ft = _____ yd

13) 84 in = _____ ft

14) 30 yd = _____ feet

Metric Capacity Measurement

✎ Convert the following measurements

1) 32 l = _____ ml

2) 7 l = _____ ml

3) 54 l = _____ ml

4) 92 l = _____ ml

5) 48 l = _____ ml

6) 13 l = _____ ml

7) 5,000 ml = _____ l

8) 10,000 ml = _____ l

9) 73,000 ml = _____ l

10) 8,000 ml = _____ l

11) 49,000 ml = _____ l

12) 25,000 ml = _____ l

Customary Capacity Measurement

✎ Convert the following measurements

1) 50 gal = _____ qt.

2) 5 gal = _____ pt.

3) 2 gal = _____ c.

4) 20 pt. = _____ c

5) 5 qt = _____ pt.

6) 3 qt = _____ c

7) 50 pt. = _____ c

8) 48 c = _____ gal

9) 96 pt. = _____ gal

10) 16 qt = _____ gal

11) 15 c = _____ fl oz

12) 44 c = _____ qt

13) 240 c = _____ pt.

14) 48 qt = _____ gal

15) 100 pt. = _____ qt

16) 2 pt. = _____ fl oz.

Metric Weight and Mass Measurement

✎ Convert.

1) 60 kg = _____ g

2) 24 kg = _____ g

3) 610 kg = _____ g

4) 82 kg = _____ g

5) 95 kg = _____ g

6) 48 kg = _____ g

7) 15 kg = _____ g

8) 95,000 g = _____ kg

9) 24,000 g = _____ kg

10) 70,000 g = _____ kg

11) 2,000 g = _____ kg

12) 28,000 g = _____ kg

13) 970,000 g = _____ kg

14) 35,000 g = _____ kg

Customary Weight and Mass Measurement

✎ Convert.

1) 10,000 lb. = _____ T

2) 18,000 lb. = _____ T

3) 32,000 lb. = _____ T

4) 16,000 lb. = _____ T

5) 5 lb. = _____ oz

6) 7 lb.= _____ oz

7) 10 lb. = _____ oz

8) 4 T = _____ lb.

9) 7 T = _____ lb.

10) 10 T = _____ lb.

11) 5 T = _____ lb.

12) 1 T = _____ oz

13) 2 T = _____ oz

14) 3 T= _____ oz

Answers of Worksheets – Chapter 6

Metric length

1) 30 cm	6) 10 m	11) 5,000 m
2) 8,000 mm	7) 200 cm	12) 2,000 cm
3) 500 cm	8) 400 cm	13) 5 km
4) 7,000 m	9) 7 m	14) 7 km
5) 9 m	10) 2,000 mm	

Customary Length

1) 96	6) 5	11) 33
2) 48	7) 4	12) 20
3) 18	8) 72	13) 7
4) 45	9) 72	14) 90
5) 1	10) 180	

Metric Capacity

1) 32,000 ml	5) 48,000 ml	9) 73 L
2) 7,000 ml	6) 13,000 ml	10) 8 L
3) 54,000 ml	7) 5 L	11) 49 L
4) 92,000 ml	8) 10 L	12) 25 L

Customary Capacity

1) 200 qt	5) 20 pt.	9) 12 gal	13) 120 pt.
2) 40 pt.	6) 24 c	10) 4 gal	14) 12 gal
3) 32 c	7) 100 c	11) 12 fl oz	15) 50 qt
4) 40 c	8) 3 gal	12) 11qt	16) 32 fl oz.

Metric Weight and Mass

1) 60,000 g	6) 48,000 g	11) 2 kg
2) 24,000 g	7) 15,000 g	12) 28 kg
3) 610,000 g	8) 95 kg	13) 970 kg
4) 82,000 g	9) 24 kg	14) 35 kg
5) 95,000g	10) 70 kg	

Customary Weight and Mass

1) 5 T	2) 9 T	3) 16 T

4) 8 T

5) 80 oz

6) 112 oz

7) 160 oz

8) 8,000 lb.

9) 14,000 lb.

10) 20,000 lb.

11) 10,000 lb.

12) 32,000 oz

13) 64,000 oz

14) 96,000 oz

Chapter 7: Patterns and sequences

Topics that you'll learn in this chapter:

- ✓ Pattern

- ✓ Growing Pattern

- ✓ Patterns Numbers

Repeating Pattern

✍ Circle the picture that comes next in each picture pattern.

1)

2)

3)

4)

5)

Growing Patterns

✍ Draw the picture that comes next in each growing pattern.

1)

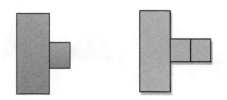

2)

3)

4)

5)

Patterns: Numbers

✍ Write the numbers that come next.

1) 2, 5, 8, 11,   _____, _____, _____, _____

2) 10, 15, 20, 25,   _____, _____, _____, _____

3) 4, 8, 12, 16,   _____, _____, _____, _____

4) 7, 17, 27, 37,   _____, _____, _____, _____

5) 5, 12, 19, 26,   _____, _____, _____, _____

6) 8, 16, 24, 32, 40,   _____, _____, _____, _____

✍ Write the next three numbers in each counting sequence.

7) –31, –19, –7, _____, _____, _____, _____

8) 541, 526, 511, _____, _____, _____, _____

9) 14, 34, _____, _____, 94, _____

10) 21, 29, _____, _____, _____

11) 89, 78, _____, _____, _____

12) 95, 82, 69, _____, _____, _____

13) 198, 166, 134, _____, _____, _____

14) What are the next three numbers in this counting sequence?

   1870, 1970, 2070, _____, _____, _____

15) What is the forth number in this counting sequence?

   8, 14, 24, _____

Answers of Worksheets – Chapter 7

Repeating pattern

1)

2)

3)

4)

5)

Growing patterns

1)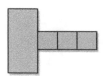

2)

3)

4)

5)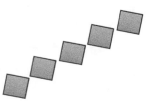

Patterns: Numbers

1) 2, 5, 8, 11, 14, 17, 20, 23

2) 10, 15, 20, 25, 30, 35, 40, 45

3) 4, 8, 12, 16, 20, 24, 28, 32

4) 7, 17, 27, 37, 47, 57, 67, 77

5) 5, 12, 19, 26, 33, 40, 47, 54

6) 8, 16, 24, 32, 40, 48, 56, 64

7) 5, 17, 29, 41

8) 496, 481, 466, 451

9) 14, 34, 54, 74, 94, 114

10) 37, 45, 53

11) 67, 56, 45

12) 56, 43, 30

13) 102, 70, 38

14) 2170, 2270, 2370

15) 30

Chapter 8: Geometric

Topics that you'll learn in this chapter:

- ✓ Identifying Angles: Acute, Right, Obtuse, and Straight Angles

- ✓ Estimate and Measure Angles with a Protractor

- ✓ Polygon Names

- ✓ Classify Triangles

- ✓ Parallel Sides in Quadrilaterals

- ✓ Identify Rectangles

- ✓ Perimeter and Area of Squares

- ✓ Perimeter and Area of rectangles

- ✓ Area and Perimeter: Word Problems

Identifying Angles

✍ Write the name of the angles (Acute, Right, Obtuse, and Straight).

1)

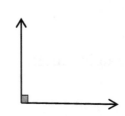

2)

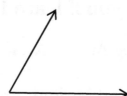

3)

4)

5)

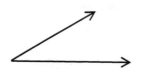

6)

7)

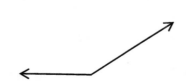

8)

Estimate Angle Measurements

✎ Estimate the approximate measurement of each angle in degrees.

2)

1)

3)

4)

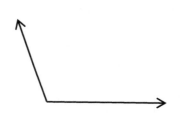

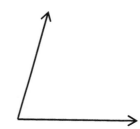

5)

6)

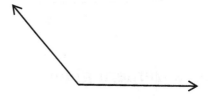

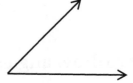

7)

8)

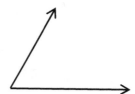

Measure Angles with a Protractor

📐Use protractor to measure the angles below.

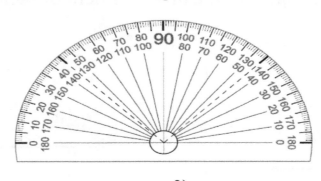

1)

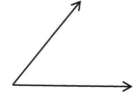

2)

3)

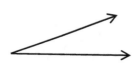

4)

📐Use a protractor to draw angles for each measurement given.

1) 140∘

2) 100∘

3) 110∘

4) 120∘

5) 55∘

Polygon Names

✎ Write name of polygons.

1)

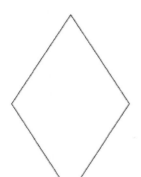

2)

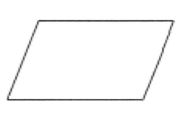

3)

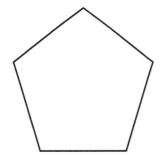

4)

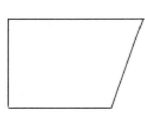

5)

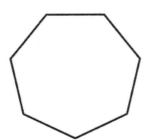

6)

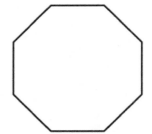

Classify Triangles

✎Classify the triangles by their sides and angles.

1)

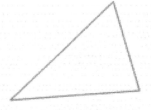

2)

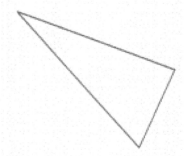

3)

4)

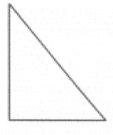

5)

6)

Parallel Sides in Quadrilaterals

✍ Write name of quadrilaterals.

1)

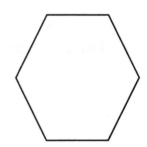

2)

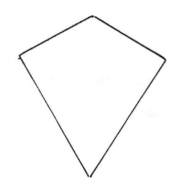

3)

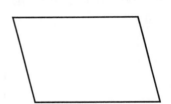

4)

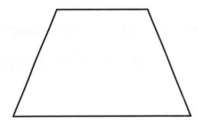

5)

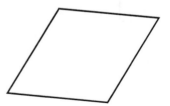

6)

Identify Rectangles

✍ Solve.

1) A square has _____ sides and _____ angles.

2) Draw a rectangle that is 5.5centimeters long and 2.5 centimeters wide. What is the perimeter?

3) Draw a rectangle 3.5 cm long and 1.5 cm wide.

4) Draw a rectangle whose length is 4.25 cm and whose width is 2.45 cm. What is the perimeter of the rectangle?

5) What is the perimeter of the rectangle?

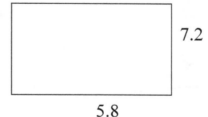

7.2

5.8

Perimeter: Find the Missing Side Lengths

✎ Find the missing side of each shape.

1) perimeter = 57.2

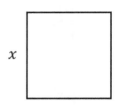

2) perimeter = 21.2

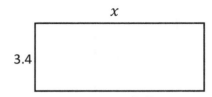

3) perimeter = 27.5

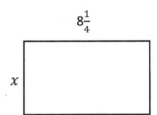

4) perimeter = 35.2

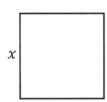

5) perimeter = 75.6

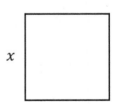

6) perimeter = 30.8

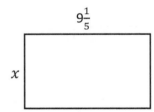

7) perimeter = 36.25

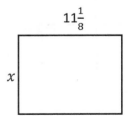

8) perimeter = 46.8

Perimeter and Area of Squares

Find perimeter and area of squares.

1) A: _____, P: _____

1.5

2) A: _____, P: _____

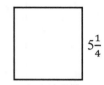

$5\frac{1}{4}$

3) A: _____, P: _____

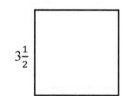

$3\frac{1}{2}$

4) A: _____, P: _____

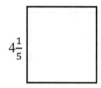

$4\frac{1}{5}$

5) A: _____, P: _____

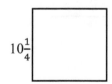

$10\frac{1}{4}$

6) A: _____, P: _____

11.3

7) A: _____, P: _____

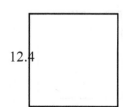

12.4

8) A: _____, P: _____

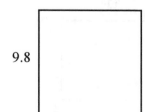

9.8

Perimeter and Area of rectangles

Find perimeter and area of rectangles.

1) A: _____, P: _____

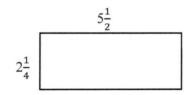

$5\frac{1}{2}$

$2\frac{1}{4}$

2) A: _____, P: _____

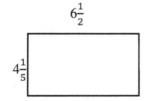

$6\frac{1}{2}$

$4\frac{1}{5}$

3) A: _____, P: _____

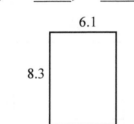

6.1

8.3

4) A: _____, P: _____

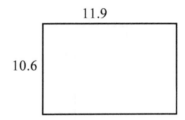

11.9

10.6

5) A: _____, P: _____

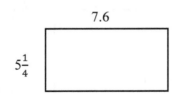

7.6

$5\frac{1}{4}$

6) A: _____, P: _____

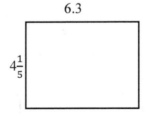

6.3

$4\frac{1}{5}$

7) A: _____, P: _____

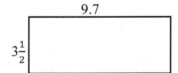

9.7

$3\frac{1}{2}$

8) A: _____, P: _____

11.4

5.8

Find the Area or Missing Side Length of a Rectangle

✍ Find area or missing side length of rectangles.

1) Area =?

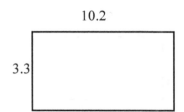

2) Area = 42.12, x=?

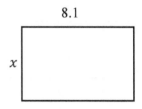

3) Area = 29.52, x=?

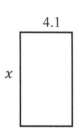

4) Area =?

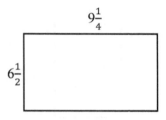

5) Area =?

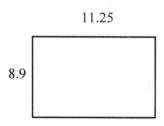

6) Area = 662.34 x=?

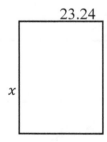

7) Area = 216.24, x=?

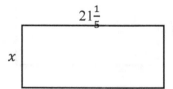

8) Area 336.42, x=?

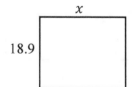

Area and Perimeter: Word Problems

✐Solve.

1) The area of a rectangle is 90.86 square meters. The width is 7.7 meters. What is the length of the rectangle?

2) A square has an area of 6.25 square feet. What is the perimeter of the square?

3) Ava built a rectangular vegetable garden that is 3.2 feet long and has an area of 21.12 square feet. What is the perimeter of Ava's vegetable garden?

4) A square has a perimeter of 12.8 millimeters. What is the area of the square?

5) The perimeter of David's square backyard is 0.96 meters. What is the area of David's backyard?

6) The area of a rectangle is 37.63 square inches. The length is 7.1 inches. What is the perimeter of the rectangle?

Answers of Worksheets – Chapter 8

Identifying Angles

1) Right	3) Obtuse	5) Acute	7) Obtuse
2) Acute	4) Straight	6) Obtuse	8) Acute

Estimate Angle Measurements

1) 160°	3) 110°	5) 130°	7) 90°
2) 180°	4) 75°	6) 45°	8) 60°

Measure Angles with a Protractor

1) 50∘	2) 135∘	3) 20∘	4) 170∘

Draw angles

1) 2) 3)

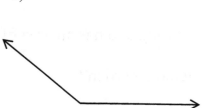 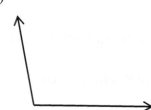 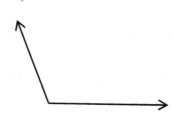

4) 5)

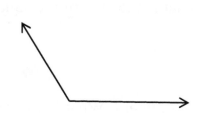 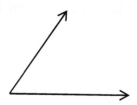

Polygon Names

1) Diamond	3) Pentagon	5) Heptagon
2) Parallelogram	4) Trapezius	6) Octagon

Classify triangles

1) Scalene, acute	4) Scalene, right
2) Isosceles, acute	5) Isosceles, right
3) Equilateral, acute	6) Scalene, obtuse

Parallel Sides in Quadrilaterals

1) Hexagon   3) Parallelogram   5) Rhombus
2) Kike   4) Trapezoid   6) Rectangle

Identify Rectangles

1) 4 - 4   3) Draw the rectangle   5) 26
2) 16   4) 13.4

Perimeter: Find the Missing Side Lengths

1) 14.3   3) 5.5   5) 18.9   7) 7
2) 7.2   4) 8.8   6) 6.2   8) 11.7

Perimeter and Area of Squares

1) A: 2.25, P: 6   4) A: 17.64, P: 16.8   7) A: 153.76, P: 49.6
2) A: 27.56, P: 21   5) A: 105.063 P: 41   8) A: 96.04, P: 39.2
3) A: 12.25, P: 14   6) A: 127.69, P: 45.2

Perimeter and Area of rectangles

1) A: 12.375, P: 15.5   4) A: 126.14, P: 45   7) A: 33.95, P: 26.4
2) A: 27.3, P: 21.4   5) A: 39.9, P: 25.7   8) A: 66.12, P: 34.4
3) A: 50.63, P: 28.8   6) A: 26.46, P: 21

Find the Area or Missing Side Length of a Rectangle

1) 33.66   3) 7.2   5) 100.125   7) 10.2
2) 5.2   4) 60.125   6) 28.5   8) 17.8

Area and Perimeter: Word Problems

1) 11.8   3) 19.6   5) 0.0576
2) 10   4) 10.24   6) 24.8

Chapter 9: Symmetry and Transformations

Topics that you'll learn in this chapter:

- ✓ Line Segments

- ✓ Identify Lines of Symmetry

- ✓ Count Lines of Symmetry

- ✓ Parallel, Perpendicular and Intersecting Lines

- ✓ Translations, Rotations, and Reflections

Line Segments

✍ Write each as a line, ray or line segment.

1)

2)

3)

4)

5)

6)

7)

8)

Identify Lines of Symmetry

✍ Tell whether the line on each shape a line of symmetry is.

1)

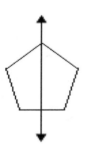

2)

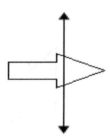

3)

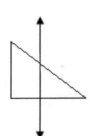

4)

5)

6)

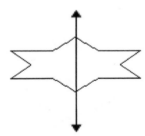

7)

8)

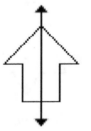

Count Lines of Symmetry

✎ Draw lines of symmetry on each shape. Count and write the lines of symmetry you see.

1)

2)

3)

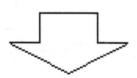

4)

5)

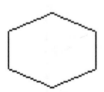

6)

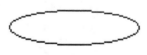

7)

8)

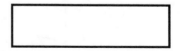

Parallel, Perpendicular and Intersecting Lines

State whether the given pair of lines are parallel, perpendicular, or intersecting.

1)

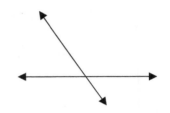

2)

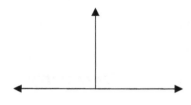

3)

4)

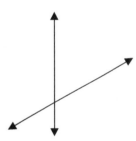

5)

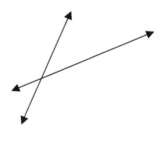

6)

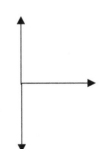

7)

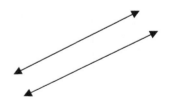

8)

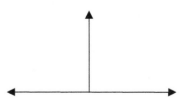

Answers of Worksheets – Chapter 9

Line Segments

1) Ray

2) Line segment

3) Line

4) Ray

5) Ray

6) Line

7) Line

8) Line segment

Identify lines of symmetry

1) yes

2) no

3) no

4) yes

5) yes

6) yes

7) no

8) yes

Count lines of symmetry

1)

2)

3)

4)

5)

6)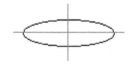

7)

8)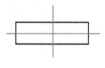

Parallel, Perpendicular and Intersecting Lines

1) Intersection

2) Perpendicular

3) Parallel

4) Intersection

5) Intersection

6) Perpendicular

7) Parallel

8) Perpendicular

Chapter 10: Data and Graphs

Topics that you'll learn in this chapter:

✓ Graph Points on a Coordinate Plane

✓ Bar Graph

✓ Tally and Pictographs

✓ Line Graphs

✓ Stem–And–Leaf Plot

Graph Points on a Coordinate Plane

Plot each point on the coordinate grid.

1) A (4, 6)	3) C (1, 5)	5) E (4, 8)
2) B (3, 2)	4) D (5, 7)	6) F (9, 2)

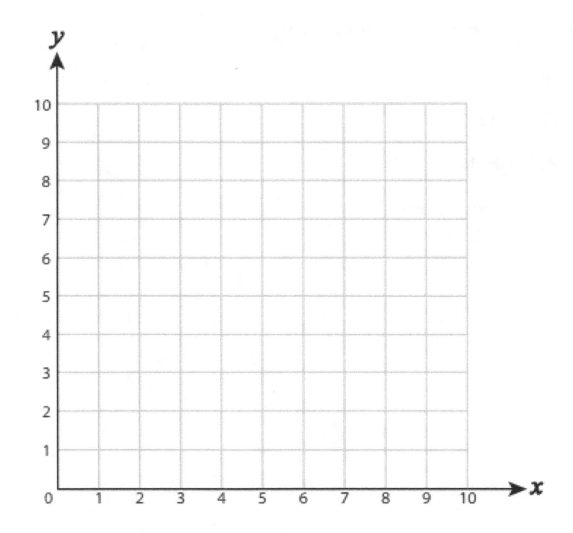

Bar Graph

✎ Graph the given information as a bar graph.

Day	Hot dogs sold
Monday	50
Tuesday	80
Wednesday	10
Thursday	30
Friday	70

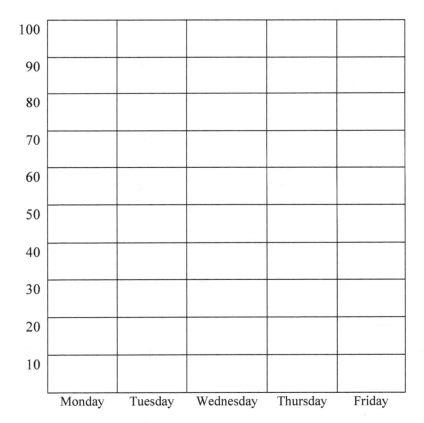

Tally and Pictographs

✎ Using the key, draw the pictograph to show the information.

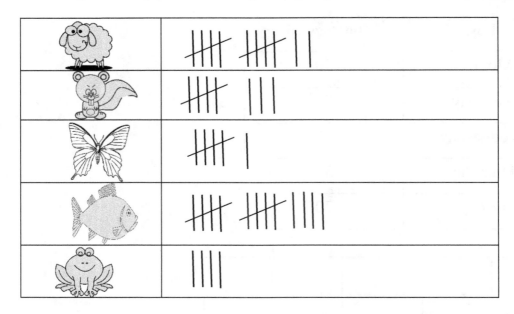

Key: ⚽   = 2 animals

Line Graphs

David work as a salesman in a store. He records the number of shoes sold in five days on a line graph. Use the graph to answer the question

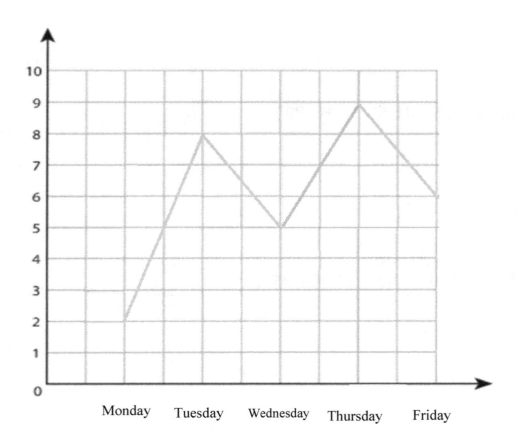

1) How many shoes were sold on Friday?

2) Which day had the minimum sales of shoes?

3) Which day had the maximum number of shoes sold?

4) How many shoes were sold in 5 days?

Stem–And–Leaf Plot

✐ Make stem ad leaf plots for the given data.

1) 40, 42, 47, 14, 19, 42, 69, 65, 49, 42, 10, 64

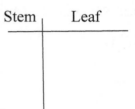

2) 43, 85, 52, 48, 45, 43, 51, 81, 59, 50, 85, 89

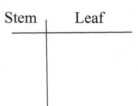

3) 112, 39, 46, 35, 80, 119, 42, 114, 37, 112, 47, 119

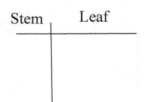

4) 90, 50, 131, 93, 112, 56, 139, 98, 115, 59, 98, 135, 111

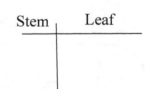

Answers of Worksheets – Chapter 10

Graph Points on a Coordinate Plane

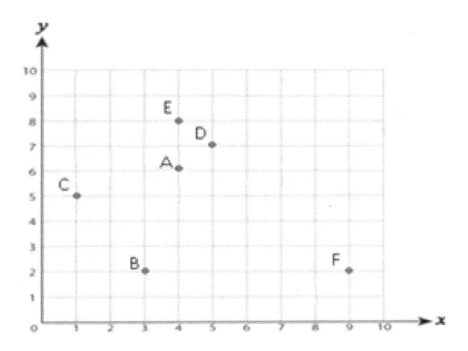

Bar Graph

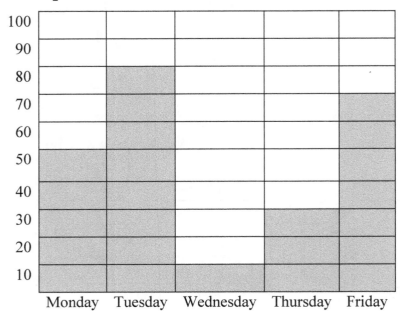

Tally and Pictographs

Line Graphs

1) 6   2) Monday   3) Thursday   4) 30

Stem–And–Leaf Plot

1)

Stem	leaf
1	0 4 9
4	2 2 2 7 9
6	4 5 9

2)

Stem	leaf
4	3 3 5 8
5	0 1 2 9
8	1 5 5 9

3)

Stem	leaf
3	5 7 9
4	2 6 7
8	0
11	2 2 4 9 9

4)

Stem	leaf
5	0 6 9
9	0 3 8 8
11	1 2 5
13	1 5 9

STAAR Math Practice Tests

Time to Test

Time to refine your skill with a practice examination

Take a REAL STAAR Mathematics test to simulate the test day experience. After you've finished, score your test using the answer key.

Before You Start

- You'll need a pencil and scratch papers to take the test.

- For this practice test, don't time yourself. Spend time as much as you need.

- It's okay to guess. You won't lose any points if you're wrong.

- After you've finished the test, review the answer key to see where you went wrong.

Calculators are not permitted for Grade 3 STAAR Tests

Good Luck!

STAAR GRADE 3 MAHEMATICS REFRENCE MATERIALS

LENGTH

Customary	Metric
1 mile (mi) = 1,760 yards (yd)	1 kilometer (km) = 1,000 meters (m)
1 yard (yd) = 3 feet (ft)	1 meter (m) = 100 centimeters (cm)
1 foot (ft) = 12 inches (in.)	1 centimeter (cm) = 10 millimeters (mm)

VOLUME AND CAPACITY

Customary	Metric
1 gallon (gal) = 4 quarts (qt)	1 liter (L) = 1,000 milliliters (mL)
1 quart (qt) = 2 pints (pt.)	
1 pint (pt.) = 2 cups (c)	
1 cup (c) = 8 fluid ounces (Fl oz)	

WEIGHT AND MASS

Customary	Metric
1 ton (T) = 2,000 pounds (lb.)	1 kilogram (kg) = 1,000 grams (g)
1 pound (lb.) = 16 ounces (oz)	1 gram (g) = 1,000 milligrams (mg)

Time

1 year = 12 months

1 year = 52 weeks

1 week = 7 days

1 day = 24 hours

1 hour = 60 minutes

1 minute = 60 seconds

State of Texas Assessments of Academic Readiness

STAAR Practice Test 1

Mathematics

GRADE 3

Administered *Month Year*

1) Classroom A contains 5 rows of chairs with 4 chairs per row. If classroom B has three times as many chairs, which number sentence can be used to find the number of chairs in classroom B?

A. $5 \times 4 + 3$

B. $5 + 4 \times 3$

C. $5 \times 4 \times 3$

D. $5 + 4 + 3$

2) There are 7 days in a week. There are 24 hours in day. How many hours are in two weeks?

A. 336

B. 168

C. 320

D. 30

3) Ella described a number using these clues:

Three-digit odd numbers that have a 7 in the hundreds place and a 3 in the tens place. Which number could fit Ella's description?

A. 723

B. 735

C. 736

D. 734

4) A cafeteria menu had spaghetti with meatballs for $7 and bean soup for $5 How much would it cost to buy two plates of spaghetti with meatballs and two bowls of bean soup?

Write your answer in the box below.

5) This clock shows a time after 8:15 PM. What time was it 3 hours and 35 minutes ago?

A. 05:40 PM

B. 05:05 PM

C. 04:45 PM

D. 04:40 PM

6) A football team is buying new uniforms. Each uniform cost $30. The team wants to buy 12 uniforms.

Which equation represents a way to find the total cost of the uniforms?

A. $(30 \times 10) + (1 \times 12) = 300 + 12$

B. $(30 \times 10) + (12 \times 1) = 300 + 12$

C. $(30 \times 10) + (30 \times 2) = 300 + 60$

D. $(12 \times 10) + (10 \times 30) = 120 + 300$

7) Olivia has 120 pastilles. She wants to put them in boxes of 6 pastilles. How many boxes does she need?

    A. 30

    B. 20

    C. 22

    D. 19

8) There are 82 students from Riddle Elementary school at the library on Tuesday. The other 33 students in the school are practicing in the classroom. Which number sentence shows the total number of students in Riddle Elementary school?

    A. $82 + 33$

    B. $82 - 33$

    C. 82×33

    D. $82 \div 33$

9) Martin earns There are 6 numbers in the box below. Which of the following list shows only odd numbers from the numbers in the box?

19, 30, 18, 28, 83, 65

    A. 19, 28, 18

    B. 19, 65, 83

    C. 19, 28, 28

    D. 30, 18, 28

10) Mia's goal is to save $120 to purchase her favorite bike.

  - In January, she saved $40.

  - In February, she saved $25.

How much money does Mia need to save in March to be able to purchase her favorite bike?

A. $40

B. $25

C. $45

D. $55

11) Michelle has 52 old books. She plans to send all of them to the library in their area. If she puts the books in boxes which can hold 4 books, which of the following equations can be used to find the number of boxes she will use?

A. $52 + 4 =$ _____

B. $52 \times 4 =$ _____

C. $52 - 4 =$ _____

D. $52 \div 4 =$ _____

12) Which number is made up of 6 hundred, 3 tens, and 5 ones?

A. 6,053

B. 635

C. 653

D. 356

13) Elise had 520 cards. Then, she gave 210 of the cards to her friend Alice. After that, Elise lost 110 cards.

Which equation can be used to find the number of cards Elise has now?

A. $520 - 210 + 110 = $ _____

B. $520 - 210 - 110 = $ _____

C. $520 + 210 + 110 = $ _____

D. $520 + 210 - 110 = $ _____

14) The length of the following rectangle is 9 centimeters and its width is 5 centimeters. What is the area of the rectangle?

A. 15 cm^2

B. 35cm^2

C. 45 cm^2

D. 28 cm^2

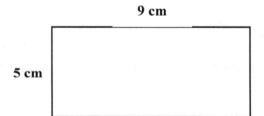

15) Look at the spinner above. On which color is the spinner most likely to land?

A. Red

B. Yellow

C. Green

D. None

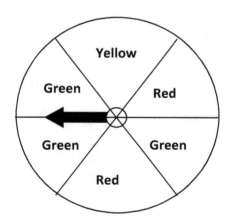

16) A group of third grade students recorded the following distances that they jumped.

22 inches	35 inches	23 inches	27 inches
35 inches	32 inches	24 inches	33 inches
31 inches	27 inches	33 inches	35 inches

What is the distance that was jumped most often?

A. 22

B. 23

C. 31

D. 35

17) Emma flew 3,124 miles from Los Angeles to New York City. What is the number of miles Emma flew rounded to the nearest thousand?

A. 4,100

B. 4,000

C. 3,100

D. 3,000

18) To what number is the arrow pointing?

A. 8

B. 7

C. 5

D. 6

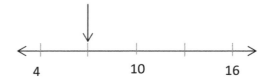

19) A number sentence such as $19 + Z = 42$ can be called an equation. If this equation is true, then which of the following equations is not true?

A. $42 - 19 = Z$

B. $42 - Z = 19$

C. $Z - 42 = 19$

D. $Z = 23$

20) Use the picture below to answer the question. Which fraction shows the shaded part of this square?

A. $\dfrac{74}{100}$

B. $\dfrac{74}{10}$

C. $\dfrac{74}{1,000}$

D. $\dfrac{7}{100}$

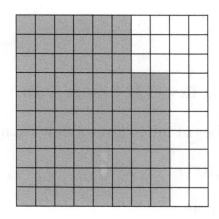

21) Which number correctly completes the number sentence $44 \times 25 = ?$

A. 810

B. 950

C. 1,050

D. 1,100

22) Which number correctly completes the subtraction sentence

$3,000 - 237 =$ _____?

A. 2,763

B. 3,521

C. 835

D. 2,251

23) Jason packs 12 boxes with flashcards. Each box holds 18 flashcards. How many flashcards Jason can pack into these boxes?

A. 261

B. 621

C. 210

D. 216

24) Which of the following statements describes the number 34,678?

A. The sum of three thousand, 4 thousand, six hundred, seventy tens, and eight ones

B. The sum of forty thousand, 3 thousand, seven hundred, six tens, and eight ones

C. The sum of thirty thousand, 4 thousand, sixty hundred, seventy tens, and eight ones

D. The sum of thirty thousand, 4 thousand, six hundred, seven tens, and eight ones

25) The following models are the same size and each divided into equal parts.

The models can be used to write two fractions.

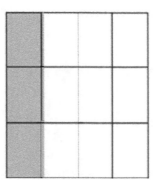 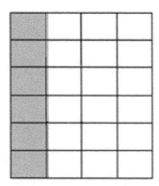

Based on the models, which of the following statements is true?

A. $\frac{3}{12}$ is bigger than $\frac{6}{24}$.

B. $\frac{3}{12}$ is smaller than $\frac{6}{24}$.

C. $\frac{3}{12}$ is equal to $\frac{6}{24}$.

D. We cannot compare these two fractions only by using the models.

26) What is the value of "A" in the following equation?

$$28 + A + 6 = 46$$

A. 13

B. 12

C. 14

D. 18

27) Emily has 90 stickers and she wants to give them to six of her closest friends. If

she gives them all an equal number of stickers, how many stickers will each of

Emily's friends receive?

Write your answer in the box below.

28) Use the models below to answer the question.

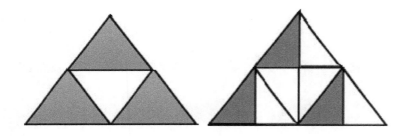

Which statement about the models is true?

A. Each shows the same fraction because they are the same size.

B. Each shows a different fraction because they are different shapes.

C. Each shows the same fraction because they both have 3 sections shaded.

D. Each shows a different fraction because they both have 3 shaded sections but

a different number of total sections.

29) Mr. smith usually eats Two meals a day. How many meals does he eat in a week?

    A. 15

    B. 14

    C. 12

    D. 21

30) What is the value of A in the equation $42 \div A = 7$?

    A. 5

    B. 7

    C. 6

    D. 9

"This is the end of the practice test 1"

State of Texas Assessments of Academic Readiness

STAAR Practice Test 2

Mathematics

GRADE 3

Administered *Month Year*

1) What number makes this equation true?

$$14 \times 6 = \square$$

A. 82

B. 84

C. 98

D. 56

2) Kayla has 110 red cards and 63 white cards. How many more reds cards than white cards do Kayla have?

A. 137

B. 173

C. 47

D. 74

3) A number sentence is shown below.

$$3 \times 5 \ \square \ 10 = 150$$

What symbol goes into the box to make the number sentence true?

A. ×

B. ÷

C. +

D. −

4) Liam had 630 marbles. Then, he gave 250 of the cards to his friend Ethan. After that, Liam lost 85 cards.

Which equation can be used to find the number of cards Eve has now?

A. 630 – 250 + 85 = ____

B. 630 – 250 – 85 = ____

C. 630 + 250 + 85 = ____

D. 630 + 250 – 85 = ____

5) What is the value of "B" in the following equation? $40 + B + 15 = 73$

A. 32

B. 56

C. 16

D. 18

6) There are two different cards on the table.

- There are 3 rows that have 17 red cards in each row.

- There are 14 white cards.

How many cards are there on the table?

A. 62

B. 65

C. 55

D. 52

7) Mason is 15 months now and he usually eats two meals a day. How many meals does he eat in a week?

    A. 12

    B. 18

    C. 14

    D. 16

8) Which of the following list shows only fractions that are equivalent to $\frac{1}{2}$?

    A. $\frac{2}{4}, \frac{7}{14}, \frac{5}{10}$

    B. $\frac{1}{3}, \frac{7}{14}, \frac{5}{10}$

    C. $\frac{5}{10}, \frac{7}{14}, \frac{4}{6}$

    D. $\frac{7}{14}, \frac{5}{10}, \frac{1}{4}$

9) What mixed number is shown by the shaded triangles?

    A. $2\frac{1}{4}$

    B. $2\frac{1}{2}$

    C. $3\frac{1}{2}$

    D. $1\frac{3}{4}$

10) The perimeter of a square is 24 units. Each side of this square is the same length.

   What is the length of one side of the square in units?

   A. 3

   B. 8

   C. 6

   D. 5

11) Which of the following comparison of fractions is true?

   A. $\frac{1}{5} = \frac{1}{6}$

   B. $\frac{1}{4} > \frac{3}{4}$

   C. $\frac{3}{7} < \frac{5}{7}$

   D. $\frac{3}{9} < \frac{1}{9}$

12) The sum of 4 ten thousand, 3 hundred, and 7 tens can be expressed as what number in standard form?

   A. 4,370

   B. 40,370

   C. 40,037

   D. 40,307

13) One side of a square is 6 feet. What is the area of the square?

   Write your answer in the box below.

   [ ]

14) What is the perimeter of the following triangle?

A. 30 inches

B. 28 inches

C. 36 inches

D. 54 inches

9 inches   15 inches

12 inches

15) Moe has 500 cards. He wants to put them in boxes of 25 cards. How many boxes does he need?

A. 22

B. 18

C. 26

D. 20

16) There are 7 rows of chairs in a classroom with 5 chairs in each row. How many chairs are in the classroom?

A. 30

B. 35

C. 32

D. 24

17) What number goes in the box to make the equation true?

$$\frac{\square}{3} = 4$$

A. 8

B. 12

C. 14

D. 16

18) Which number is represented by A?

$12 \times A = 144$

A. 15

B. 9

C. 12

D. 13

19) What is the perimeter of this rectangle?

A. 13 cm

B. 22 cm

C. 28 cm

D. 24 cm

7 cm

4 cm

20) Nicole has 2 quarters, 3 dimes, and 5 pennies. How much money does Nicole have?

    A. 80 pennies

    B. 85 pennies

    C. 70 pennies

    D. 75 pennies

21) Noah packs 30 boxes with crayons. Each box holds 14 crayons. How many crayons Noah can pack into these boxes?

    A. 480

    B. 520

    C. 510

    D. 420

22) A number sentence such as $67 - x = 36$ can be called an equation. If this equation is true, then which of the following equations is **NOT** true?

    A. $67 - 36 = x$

    B. $67 - x = 36$

    C. $x - 36 = 67$

    D. $x + 36 = 67$

23) There are 6 numbers in the box below. Which of the following list shows only even numbers from the numbers in the box?

$$13, 22, 48, 17, 70, 31$$

A. $13, 22, 48$

B. $13, 31, 70$

C. $13, 22, 70$

D. $48, 22, 70$

24) A cafeteria menu had spaghetti with meatballs for $15 and bean soup for $5. How much would it cost to buy five plates of spaghetti with meatballs and two bowls of bean soup?

Write your answer in the box below.

25) Which number correctly completes the number sentence $12 \times 55 =$?

A. 620

B. 660

C. 1,320

D. 1,200

26) There are 60 minutes in an hour. How many minutes are in 2 hours?

    A. 120 minutes

    B. 200 minutes

    C. 360 minutes

    D. 140 minutes

27) Which number correctly completes the number sentence $32 \times 15 =$?

    A. 520

    B. 580

    C. 480

    D. 420

28) Michael has 547 marbles. What is this number rounded to the nearest ten?

Write your answer in the box below.

29) Use the picture below to answer the question.

Which fraction shows the shaded part of this square?

    A. $\frac{72}{100}$

    B. $\frac{72}{10}$

    C. $\frac{7.2}{100}$

    D. $\frac{0.72}{100}$

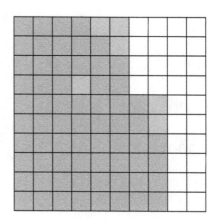

30) Use the table below to answer the question.

Based on their populations, which list of cities is in order from least to greatest?

A. Bryan; Edinburg; Longview; Mission

B. Bryan; Longview; Edinburg; Mission

C. Edinburg; Mission; Longview; Bryan

D. Longview; Edinburg; Mission; Bryan

City Populations	
City	**Population**
Bryan	14,021
Mission	14,905
Longview	14,206
Edinburg	14,408

"This is the end of practice test 2"

Answers and Explanations

STAAR Practice Tests

Answer Key

❋ Now, it's time to review your results to see where you went wrong and what areas you need to improve!

STAAR - Mathematics

Practice Test - 1						Practice Test - 2					
1	C	11	D	21	D	1	B	11	C	21	D
2	A	12	B	22	A	2	C	12	B	22	C
3	B	13	B	23	D	3	A	13	36	23	D
4	24	14	C	24	D	4	B	14	C	24	85
5	D	15	C	25	C	5	D	15	D	25	B
6	C	16	D	26	B	6	B	16	B	26	A
7	B	17	D	27	15	7	C	17	B	27	C
8	A	18	B	28	D	8	A	18	C	28	550
9	B	19	C	29	B	9	B	19	B	29	A
10	D	20	A	30	C	10	D	20	B	30	B

Practice Test 1
STAAR - Mathematics
Answers and Explanations

1) Answer: C.

Classroom A contains 5 rows of chairs with four chairs per row. Therefore, there are (5 × 4 =) 20 chairs in Classroom A. Classroom B has three times as many chairs. Then, there are (5 × 4 × 3) chairs in Classroom B.

2) Answer: A.

1 day: 24 hours

7 days = 7 × 24 = 168 hours, for two weeks: 2 × 168 = 336

3) Answer: B.

Three-digit odd numbers that have a 7 in the hundreds place and a 3 in the tens place is 735. 734 and 738 are even numbers.

4) Answer: 24.

2 plates of spaghetti with meatballs cost: 2 × $7 = $14

2 bowls of bean soup cost: 2 × $5 = $10

2 plates of spaghetti with meatballs + 2 bowls of bean soup cost: $14 + $10 = $24

5) Answer: D.

The clock shows 8:15 PM. 3 hours before that was 5:15 PM. 35 minutes before that was 4:40 PM.

6) Answer: C.

The Football team buys 12 uniforms that each uniform cost $30. Therefore, they should pay (12 × $30 =) $360.

Choice C is the correct answer. (30 × 10) + (30 × 2) = 300 + 60 = 360

7) Answer: B.

Olivia wants to put 120 pastilles into boxes of 6 pastilles.

Therefore, she needs (120 ÷ 6 =) 20 boxes.

8) Answer: A.

To find the total number of students in Riddle Elementary School, add 82 with 33.

9) Answer: B.

An easy way to tell whether a large number is odd or even is to look at its final digit. If the number ends with an odd digit (1, 3, 5, 7, or 9), then it's odd. On the other hand, if the number ends with an even digit or 0 (0, 2, 4, 6 or 8), then it is even.

19, 83 and 65 ends with odd digit, therefore, they are odd numbers.

10) Answer: D.

Mia saved $40 and $25. Therefore, she has $65 now.

$120 − $65 = $55. She needs to save 55.

11) Answer: D.

Michelle puts 52 books in 4 boxes. Therefore, $52 \div 4$ formula is correct.

12) Answer: B.

To find the number, put 6 for hundreds place, 3 for tens place, and 5 for one's place.

Then, you will get: $600 + 30 + 5 = 635$

13) Answer: B.

Elise gave 210 of her 520 cards to her friend. Therefore, she has $520 - 210$ cards now.

Then she lost 110 cards. Now, she has $(520 - 210 - 110) = 200$ cards

14) Answer: C.

Use area formula of a rectangle:

Area = length × width

Area = $5cm \times 9cm = 45$ cm^2

15) Answer: C.

The chance of landing on red is 2 out of 6.

The chance of landing on yellow is 1 out of 6.

The chance of landing on green is 3 out of 6.

The chance of landing on green is more than the chance of landing on other colors.

16) Answer: D.

35 is the most frequent number in the table.

17) Answer: D.

The number 3,124 rounded to the nearest thousand is 3,000.

18) Answer: B.

The arrow shows a number between two numbers 4 and 10. $(10 - 4 = 6, 6 \div 2 = 3) \Rightarrow 4 + 3 = 7$

Therefore, the answer is 7.

19) Answer: C.

$19 + Z = 42$. Then, $Z = (42 - 19 =) 23$.

All these equations are true:

$42 - 19 = Z$

$42 - Z = 19$

$Z = 23$

But this equation is not true: $Z - 42 = 19$

20) Answer: A.

The table is divided into 100 equal parts. 74 parts of these 100 parts are shaded. The shaded part is equal to $\frac{74}{100}$.

21) Answer: D.

$44 \times 25 = 1,100$

22) Answer: A.

$3,000 - 237 = 2,763$

23) Answer: D.

To find the answer, multiply 12 by 18.

$12 \times 18 = 216$

24) Answer: D.

34,678 is the sum of:

$30,000 + 4,000 + 600 + 70 + 8$

25) Answer: C.

The first model is divided into 12 equal parts. 3 out of 12 parts are shaded. That means $\frac{3}{12}$ which is equal to: $\frac{1}{4}$

The second model is divided into 24 equal parts. 6 out of 24 parts are shaded. That means $\frac{6}{24}$ which is equal to: $\frac{1}{4}$

26) Answer: B.

$A = 46 - 28 - 6 = 12$

27) Answer 15.

$90 \div 6 = 15$

28) Answer: D.

The first model from left is divided into 4 equal parts. 3 out of 4 parts are shaded. The fraction for this model is $\frac{3}{4}$. The second model is divided into 8 equal parts. 3 out of 8 parts are shaded. Therefore, the fraction of the shaded parts for this model is $\frac{3}{8}$. These two models represent different fractions.

29) Answer: B.

2 meals a day, means $(2 \times 7 =)$ 14 meals a week.

30) Answer: C.

$A = 42 \div 7 = 6$

Practice Test 2
STAAR - Mathematics
Answers and Explanations

1) Answer: B.

$14 \times 6 = 84$

2) Answer: C.

To find the answer subtract 63 from 110. The answer is $(110 - 63) = 47$.

3) Answer: A.

$3 \times 5 = 15$. Then:

$3 \times 5 \; \square \; 10 = 150$

$15 \; \square \; 10 = 150 \Rightarrow 150 = 15 \times 10$

4) Answer: B.

Liam gave 250 of his marbles to his friend. Now he has $630 - 250 = 380$

He lost 85 of his marbles. Now, he has $380 - 85 = 295$ or $(630 - 250 - 85)$.

5) Answer: D.

$40 + B + 15 = 73 \Rightarrow 55 + B = 73 \Rightarrow B = 73 - 55 = 18$

6) Answer: B.

3 rows that have 17 red cards in each row contain: $3 \times 17 = 51$ red cards

And there are 14 white cards on table. Therefore, there are $51 + 14 = 65$ cards on table.

7) Answer: C.

If Mason eats 2 meals in 1 day, then, in a week (7days) he eats $(7 \times 2 = 14)$ meals.

8) Answer: A.

All these fractions $\frac{2}{4}, \frac{7}{14}, \frac{5}{10}$ are equivalent to $\frac{1}{2}$.

9) Answer: B.

This shape shows 2 complete shaded triangles and 2 parts of a triangle divided into 4 equal parts. It is equal to $2\frac{1}{2}$.

10) Answer: D.

Perimeter of the square is 24. Then:

$24 = 4 \times \text{side} \Rightarrow \text{side} = 6$

Each side of the square is 6 units.

11) Answer: C.

Only option C is correct.

12) Answer: B.

4 ten thousand = 40,000

3 hundred = 300

7 tens = 70

Add all: 40,000 + 300 + 70 = 40,370

13) Answer: 36.

To find the area of a square, multiply one side by itself.

Area of a square = (side) × (side) = 6 × 6 = 36

14) Answer: C.

To find the perimeter of the triangle, add all three sides.

Perimeter = 9 + 12 + 15 = 36 inches

15) Answer: D.

Moe wants to put 500 cards into boxes of 25 cards. Therefore, he needs (500 ÷ 25 =) 20 boxes.

16) Answer: B.

7 rows of chairs with 5 chairs in each row means: 7 × 5 = 35 chairs in total.

17) Answer: B.

We need to find a number that when divided by 3, the answer is 4. Therefore, we are looking for 12.

18) Answer: C.

$A = 144 \div 12 \Rightarrow A = 12$

19) Answer: B.

Use perimeter of rectangle formula.

Perimeter = 2 × length + 2 × width ⇒ P= 2 × 4 + 2 × 7 = 8 +14 = 22 cm

20) Answer: B.

2 quarters = 2 × 25 pennies = 50 pennies

3 dimes = 3 × 10 pennies = 30 pennies

In total Nicole has 85 pennies

21) Answer: D.

30 × 14 = 420

22) Answer: C.

$67 - x = 36$

Then, $x = 67 - 36 = 31$

Let's review the equations provided:

A. $67 - 36 = x$ This is true!

B. $67 - x = 36$ This is true!

C. $x - 36 = 67$ This is NOT true!

D. $x + 36 = 67$ This is true!

23) Answer: D.

Even numbers always end with a digit 0, 2, 4, 6 or 8.

Therefore, numbers 48, 22, 70 are the only even numbers.

24) Answer: 85.

5 spaghettis with meatballs cost: 5 × $15 = $75

2 bowls of bean soup cost: 2 × $5 = $10

5 spaghettis with meatballs + 2 bowls of bean soup cost: $75 + $ 10 = $85

25) Answer: B.

12 × 55 = 660

26) Answer: A.

1 hour = 60 minutes

2 hours = 2 × 60 minutes ⇒ 2hours = 120 minutes

27) Answer: C.

$32 \times 15 = 480$

28) Answer: 550.

We round the number up to the nearest ten if the last digit in the number is 5, 6, 7, 8, or 9.

We round the number down to the nearest ten if the last digit in the number is 1, 2, 3, or 4.

If the last digit is 0, then we do not have to do any rounding, because it is already rounded to the ten.

Therefore, rounded number of 547 to the nearest ten is 550.

29) Answer: A.

The table is divided into 100 equal parts. 72 parts of these 100 parts are shaded. It means $\frac{72}{100}$.

30) Answer: B.

Bryan city with 14,021 has the least population. Longview, Edinburg and Mission are other cities in order from least to greatest.

"End"

Printed in the USA
CPSIA information can be obtained
at www.ICGtesting.com
LVHW011109041123
762561LV00053B/201